GENERAL CHEMISTRY PROBLEMS

GENERAL CHEMISTRY

PROBLEMS

WILLIAM M. SPICER

PROFESSOR OF CHEMISTRY
GEORGIA SCHOOL OF TECHNOLOGY

WILLIAM S. TAYLOR

PROFESSOR OF CHEMISTRY
GEORGIA SCHOOL OF TECHNOLOGY

JOE D. CLARY

SUPERINTENDENT, SPECIALTY CATALYST PLANT
DAVISON CHEMICAL CORPORATION

NEW YORK

JOHN WILEY & SONS, INC.

CHAPMAN & HALL, LTD.

LONDON

PREFACE

In this problem book we attempt to teach:

1. The necessity for the justification of every step taken in the solution of a problem. In this way purely mechanical operations must be avoided. The object in working chemical problems is not so much to learn to work problems as to learn something by working them. Problem work should teach the use of the laws and principles of chemistry and should also teach the student to reason logically and rigorously from a premise (law, definition, or assumption) to a conclusion. We still believe that hard work has its rewards and that these rewards can be obtained in no other way.

2. The importance of thinking in terms of chemical units or quantity, moles, gram-atomic weights, gram-equivalent weights, etc. This process clarifies the student's thinking and often shortens his work. The best interpretation of the equation

$$2KClO_3 = 2KCl + 3O_2$$

is that two moles of $KClO_3$ yield two moles of KCl and three moles of O_2. This is a simple relation. Why should we attempt to teach our students to interpret this as "2×122.553 g. of $KClO_3$ yield 2×74.553 g. of KCl and 3×32 g. of oxygen"?

3. The elementary ideas about significant figures. Freshmen not only can be taught to use the simplest conventions regarding the number of figures to be retained but also by means of illustrations can be convinced of the essential correctness of these conventions. This knowledge should give students a clearer understanding of the meaning of scientific data.

4. The use of logarithms and the slide rule. Most students who are unacquainted with these methods lose their enthusiasm for problem work when the problems begin to involve much multiplication and division. They feel that the gain is not worth the time and effort.

5. The importance of mentally checking all results. In this way entirely unreasonable answers can be avoided. The student

should learn that to give an unreasonable answer is worse than giving no answer at all.

It is our hope that this presentation will furnish the student with grounds for mental growth, and it is our belief that his rewards will be proportional to his efforts. We shall welcome criticisms and suggestions.

We wish to acknowledge our great indebtedness to Professor John L. Daniel for his encouragement and wise advice. Our thanks are also due to Mr. Dice R. Anderson, who read the entire manuscript.

W. M. SPICER
W. S. TAYLOR
J. D. CLARY

Georgia School of Technology
Atlanta, Georgia
April 1, 1943

CONTENTS

INTRODUCTION

The first thing that you should learn, if you have not already done so, is that all education is self-education. You must do the learning. The purpose of this workbook is to help you teach yourself.

One of the main difficulties faced by students of elementary chemistry is that of working problems. The difficulty is not in the mathematics, which usually amounts to a few simple multiplications and divisions, but is due to a lack of understanding of the principles upon which the problems are based, an inability to be exact, and a tendency to work problems by a thoughtless and mechanical process rather than by reasoning.

If you are a critical individual you may well ask, "What is the purpose of problems, anyway? If I can obtain the correct numerical answer to every problem assigned, does this necessarily mean that I have attained all that might be attained in this regard? In short, is the numerical answer all important?"

In answering, let us say that the correct numerical answer is important, but it is not all-important, nor is it even the most important thing. Our main purpose in assigning you problems is to teach you to *reason rigorously and to make exact statements*. Most students seem to think that the difference between a problem and a discussion question is that the problem involves a large amount of calculation towards the end of obtaining the correct numerical answer. This is not true. The essential difference is that the problem involves rigorous and exact reasoning from a premise (law, definition, or assumption) to a conclusion. One must be explicit and definite.

In order to attain this end, we require you, in working problems, to justify each step *in writing* by reference to a law or definition, or by mathematical reasoning. To do this, the student need only ask himself, "Why?" at each step in the problem and then answer the query on paper. This, of course, involves label-

1

ing all the intermediate and final answers. If a student can work a given problem in this way, we are justified in believing that he is capable of solving other problems of the same type, because all problems of one type are based on the same principle, and the student has not only demonstrated his knowledge of the principle by stating it in writing but has also shown that he knows what the principle means by applying it to a given numerical problem. (The latter, of course, is more important because even a parrot can memorize a combination of words and restate them when called upon.) However, if the student works the problem by merely jotting down some figures, even if he works a large number of these, the instructor can never be quite sure that the student knows what he is doing.

There are two other requirements that must be fulfilled for a perfect solution to a problem. (1) The problem must not be worked by a method that will likely lead to error, or, at least, to unnecessary difficulties in the future. In regard to such methods and difficulties, we ask you to have faith in the advice of your instructor. This advice is based upon years of experience with many students. (2) Other things being equal, the shortest solution is the best one. In order to shorten your work and clarify your thinking, we suggest that you work in terms of chemical units (gram-molecular weights, gram-atomic weights, and gram-equivalent weights) instead of in terms of arbitrary physical units such as grams and pounds.

To summarize, then, we feel that for a perfect solution the following requirements must have been fulfilled.

1. The correct answer has been obtained and correctly labeled.

2. Each step has been justified in writing.

3. No method has been used that might lead to future errors or difficulties.

4. The problem has not been worked by a long laborious process when a shorter and clearer method should have been obvious to the student.

Perhaps some student will feel that in making four definite requirements of him we are tending to curb his originality. This is obviously not our purpose. In fact, we wish to foster originality and feel that a student can fulfil the above requirements and still be original.

Now that we have stated the requirements necessary for a perfect solution of a problem, you may well ask what method we intend using. Our method—if a method at all—will become clear later in the many illustrative problems. In fact, we avoid a definite method because when a student is given a method he emphasizes the method and forgets the problem, which is the important thing. *We hope that you will think each new problem through step by step for yourself.* In this way you will learn to think for yourself and have confidence in your own ability.

Perhaps you will be surprised or disappointed to find such simple problems in the early exercises. They were made simple because *we wish to emphasize excellence.* When you have an exercise to hand in, first work it out on a separate sheet, work it over to improve it in the light of the four requirements given above, and then copy it neatly.

It is not likely that this introduction has made much impression on you at first reading, nor is it likely that you will retain much that it has said. It is important, however, in that it not only makes suggestions but states a point of view.

CHAPTER I

CONVERSION OF UNITS, DENSITY, PERCENTAGE

Units are simple standard quantities in terms of which other quantities of the same class can be expressed. You are familiar with the foot, the yard, and the mile as units of length. Any length can be expressed in terms of a certain number of feet, yards, or miles. Of course, if you know a given length in terms of one of these units, you can express it in terms of any other one. For example, 220 yards equals 660 feet.

In scientific work, instead of these familiar units, the C.G.S. system of units is more often used. (C.G.S. stands for Centimeter-Gram-Second.) In this system, the unit of length is the meter. The meter was originally defined as one ten-millionth of the distance between the equator and the North Pole. One hundredth of a meter is called a centimeter and is abbreviated cm. The unit volume is the centimeter cubed (cc.),* and one thousand cubic centimeters is called a liter. The unit of mass (or weight) is the gram. This is the mass of 1 cc. of water at 4° C. (On the centigrade temperature scale water freezes at 0° and boils at 100°.) The relation between the various units is given in the table below. You are expected to remember those in italics.

Length

1 kilometer	*= 1000 meters*
1 meter	*= 100 centimeters (cm.)*
1 centimeter	*= 10 millimeters (mm.)*
1 mile	= 1.60935 kilometers (km.)
1 yard	= 0.91440 meter
1 foot	= 30.4801 cm.
1 inch	= 2.5400 cm.

* Sometimes you will encounter the abbreviation ml. For the present, you may consider ml. and cc. as the same.

4

VOLUME

1 liter	*= 1000 cubic centimeters (cc.)*
1 cubic inch	= 16.387 cc.
1 cubic foot	= 0.02832 cu. meter
1 cubic yard	= 0.76456 cu. meter
1 quart	= 0.94633 liter (l.)
1 gallon	= 3.78533 liters

WEIGHT

1 kilogram	*= 1000 grams (g.)*
1 pound	= 453.59 grams
1 ounce	= 28.3495 grams
1 ton	= 2000 lb.

Illustrative Problems

1. Two pounds of salt contains how many grams?

Solution. There are 453.6 g. in 1 lb.; therefore there are $2 \times 453.6 =$ 907.2 g. in 2 lb.   *Ans.* 907.2 g.

2. How many pounds of salt are 1700 g.?

Solution. A given weight in grams equals weight in pounds times the number of grams in 1 lb., or

$$\text{Weight in pounds} = \frac{\text{Weight in grams}}{\text{Grams in 1 lb.}} = \frac{1700}{453.6} = 3.748 \text{ lb.}$$

Ans. 3.748 lb.

Problems

1. One ton of lead is how many grams?   *Ans.* 907,180 g.

2. If table salt is worth one cent per hundred grams, what is its value per pound?   *Ans.* 4.5 cents.

3. Which had you rather have, 0.1 oz. of gold or 2 g. of gold?

4. How many cubic centimeters are there in 1 cu. meter?

Ans. 1,000,000 cc.

5. One cubic meter is how many liters? How many quarts?

6. If 1 mole (a chemical unit of quantity) of salt is 58.5 g., how many moles of salt are there in 150 g.?   *Ans.* 2.56 moles.

7. One pound of salt is how many moles?

8. What is the weight in grams of 5 moles of salt?

9. If your average walking step is two-thirds meter, how many steps would you take in walking 1 mile?

10. One liter is how many cubic inches?

DENSITY

We have just learned how to convert cubic centimeters into liters. If we are given a volume in cubic centimeters we can easily express this volume in liters. The next question is: Given the volume of a substance, can its weight be calculated? Obviously, more information is necessary for this calculation. To a given volume expressed in cubic centimeters there corresponds one and only one volume in liters. To say you have a volume of 1500 cc. is the same as saying that you have a volume of 1.5 liters. But to a given volume there does not correspond one and only one weight. For example, 1500 cc. of water weighs 1500 grams, 1500 cc. of gold weighs 29,500 grams, while this volume of hydrogen gas weighs only 0.135 gram. Thus, merely to state the volume of something is to give very little information concerning its weight. More knowledge is necessary. Suppose you were given, besides the volume, the weight of 1 cc., or the weight of any number of cubic centimeters, you would be able to calculate the weight of any given volume, since

Total weight =

Weight of 1 cc. × Number of cubic centimeters   (1)

This weight * of 1 cc. of substance is called its density and is represented by the symbol D. Similarly, representing weight by W, and volume by V, relation (1) becomes

$$W = D \times V \qquad (2)$$

or

$$D = \frac{W}{V} \qquad (3)$$

or

$$V = \frac{W}{D} \qquad (4)$$

If any two of these variables are known, the other one can be calculated.

* When we weigh a substance on a chemical balance we obtain its mass and not its weight. But in chemical literature, the word "weight" is usually used in the sense of mass, so we shall use it here.

Perry Downen

We have just defined density as the weight of 1 cc. In general, density is weight per unit volume, as defined by equation 3. It follows from equation 3 that the units of density are those of weight divided by volume. In dealing with density as well as with other quantities, units should be attached. Thus the density of water is 1 gram per cc. or 1 kg. per liter. The density of lead is 11.4 g. per cc. (Grams per cubic centimeter is often written g/cc.)

Changes of Density with Temperature and Pressure. The density of a solid or a liquid changes very slightly with changes in temperature or pressure since their volumes change only slightly. (The weight, of course, does not change at all.) But the volume of a gas, and therefore the density, is dependent on the temperature and pressure. For example, if a liter of a gas at 0° C. and ordinary atmospheric pressure (760 mm. of mercury) is heated, without changing the pressure, to 273° C., the volume will be two liters, and since the weight is unchanged, the density will be halved. Therefore, in dealing with the density of gases, not only the units but also the conditions of temperature and pressure should be stated. Thus the density of air at one atmosphere and 0° C. is 1.293 g/l. This subject will be discussed fully under "Gas Laws" (Chap. IV).

Illustrative Problems

1. If 44.0 g. of a gas, carbon dioxide, occupies 22.4 l. at 1 atmosphere pressure and 0° C., what is its density?

Solution. By definition,

$$D = \frac{W}{V} = \frac{44.0 \text{ g.}}{22.4 \text{ l.}} = 1.96 \text{ g/l. at 760 mm. and } 0° \text{ C.}$$

Ans. 1.96 g/l.

2. What volume of carbon dioxide at 0° C. and 760 mm. weighs 10.0 g.?

Solution. The density of carbon dioxide under these conditions is 1.96 g/l. From the definition of density

$$D = \frac{W}{V}$$

it follows that

$$V = \frac{W}{D} = \frac{10.0}{1.96} \text{ l.} = 5.10 \text{ l.} \qquad Ans. \text{ 5.10 l.}$$

3. At 273° C. and 380 mm. pressure the density of carbon dioxide is 0.49 g/l. What is the weight of 17 l.?

Solution. Since

$$D = \frac{W}{V}$$

then

$$W = D \times V = 0.49 \times 17 = 8.3 \text{ g.} \qquad Ans. \text{ 8.3 g.}$$

Problems

1. At zero degrees and 760 mm. pressure 520 cc. of oxygen weighs 0.740 g. Calculate its density in grams per cubic centimeter and in grams per liter. *Ans.* 0.00142 g/cc., 1.42 g/l.

2. The densest substance known is the rare metal osmium; 12.0 cc. of this metal weighs 270 g. What is its density? *Ans.* 22.5 g/cc.

3. The lighest substance known is the gas hydrogen, 1 l. of which, at 0° C. and 760 mm., weighs only 0.0899 g. One gram of hydrogen occupies what volume? *Ans.* 11.1 l.

4. (*a*) What is the weight of 1 l. of osmium? (See problem 2.)
Ans. 22,500 g.

(*b*) What is the weight in grams of 1 cu. ft. of osmium?
Ans. 637,000 g.

(*c*) What is the weight in pounds of 1 cu. ft. of osmium?
Ans. 1410 lb.

(*d*) What volume of osmium could you lift? Give reason for your answer.

5. What is the density of lead in pounds per cubic foot?

6. If the volume of a given weight of gas is doubled, what happens to the density? Why?

7. Suppose someone told you that he had a single liter of a substance that weighed 25,000 g. and a liter of another substance that weighed only 0.01 g. under ordinary conditions. Would you think him mistaken? If so, why?

8. (*a*) If the density of hydrogen sulfate is 1.8 g/cc., what is the weight of 1 l. of this substance?

(*b*) If one mole of hydrogen sulfate weighs 98 g., how many moles are there in 1 l.?

9. What is the density of a substance 750 cc. of which weighs 1500 g.?

10. What volume of hydrogen sulfate, whose density is 1.8 g/cc. will weigh 25 g.?

PERCENTAGE

By per cent (%) is meant parts in 100 parts. Thus the statement that 52 per cent of the population of Atlanta is women means that out of every hundred people, 52 are women. Notice that per cent is 100 times the fraction. Women make up a fraction of 52/100 of the population, and a percentage, therefore, of $\frac{52}{100} \times 100 = 52$. Thus, in general

$$\text{Per cent } A = \text{Parts } A \text{ in } 100 \text{ total parts}$$

$$= \text{Parts } A \text{ in } 1 \text{ part} \times 100$$

$$\text{Per cent } A = \text{Fraction which is } A \times 100$$

$$= \frac{\text{Parts } A}{\text{Parts total}} \times 100 \tag{5}$$

Illustrative Problems

1. A school having a total enrollment of 2500 students has a senior class of 450.

(a) What fraction of the students is seniors? (b) What percentage is seniors?

$$\text{Fraction seniors} = \frac{\text{Number of seniors}}{\text{Total number of students}}$$

$$= \frac{450}{2500} = 0.180 \qquad Ans. \ (a) \ 0.180.$$

(b) By definition of per cent,

$$\text{Per cent seniors} = 100 \times \text{Fraction of seniors}$$

$$= 100 \times 0.180 = 18.0 \quad Ans. \ (b) \ 18.0.$$

or

$$\text{Per cent seniors} = \frac{\text{Number of seniors}}{\text{Total number of students}} \times 100$$

$$= \frac{450}{2500} \times 100 = 18.0$$

2. There are 32.06 g. of sulfur in 98.08 g. of hydrogen sulfate. What is the percentage of sulfur in hydrogen sulfate?

$$\text{Per cent sulfur} = \frac{\text{Weight of sulfur}}{\text{Total weight of compound}} \times 100$$

$$= \frac{32.06}{98.08} \times 100 = 32.69 \quad Ans.$$

3. Hydrogen sulfate is 32.69 per cent sulfur. What weight of hydrogen sulfate contains 20.0 g. of sulfur?

Solution. Let W = weight of hydrogen sulfate which contains 20 g. sulfur, then

$$32.69\% \ W = 20.0$$

or

$$0.3269W = 20.0$$

$$W = \frac{20.0}{0.3269} = 61.2 \text{ g.} \quad Ans.$$

Problems

1. One is what percentage of a dozen?   *Ans.* 8.33.

2. If 44.00 g. of carbon dioxide contain 12.00 g. of carbon, what is the percentage of carbon in carbon dioxide?   *Ans.* 27.27.

3. What weight of carbon dioxide contains 22.00 g. of carbon?
          Ans. 80.67 g.

4. What weight of hydrogen sulfate could be made from 10 g. of sulfur? See example 3.

5. What weight of carbon dioxide, which is 27.27 per cent carbon, could be made from 10 g. of carbon?

6. A 2.00 per cent salt solution has a density of 1.01 g/cc. What is the weight of salt in 1 l. of solution?

7. What volume of a 20 per cent salt solution having a density of 1.1 g/cc. could be prepared from 10 g. of salt?   *Ans.* 45.5 cc.

8. The density of silver is 10.5 g/cc. What is the weight of a cube of silver which is 2 cm. on an edge?   *Ans.* 84 g.

9. A cylinder of Cu, 4 cm. in diameter and 5 cm. high, weighs 560.5 g. What is the density of Cu?   *Ans.* 8.92 g/cc.

10. An old iron cannon ball (sphere) has a diameter of 12 cm. The density of iron is 7.86 g/cc. What is the weight of the ball?
          Ans. 7112 g.

11. What would be the diameter of an aluminum sphere having the same weight as the cannon ball in the previous problem? The density of Al is 2.70 g/cc.

12. A certain sand is 90 per cent silicon dioxide. Silicon dioxide is 46.7 per cent silicon. What weight of silicon (in grams) is contained in 1 lb. of this sand?

13. What weight of sand (in ⚹ 12) contains 1 g. of silicon?

CHAPTER II

EQUIVALENT WEIGHTS *

We have seen that the elements combine with one another to form compounds. The metals iron and copper both combine with oxygen of the air to form oxides. The element carbon (charcoal) will burn in air, combining with oxygen to form carbon dioxide. Hydrogen combines with oxygen to form water. Now there arises the question, "Does the same weight of each of these elements react with the same weight of oxygen?" The answer is "No." By experiment we find that 18.61 grams of iron, 31.79 grams of copper, 3.003 grams of carbon, and 1.008 grams of hydrogen combine separately with 8 grams of oxygen.† From a chemical standpoint we say that 18.61 grams of iron, 31.79 grams of copper, 3.003 grams of carbon, and 1.008 grams of hydrogen are equivalent to one another in that these weights of these four elements accomplish the same thing, i.e., combine with 8 grams of oxygen. If you had 8 grams of oxygen which you wished to get into combination with something, it is obvious that 18.61 grams of iron, 31.79 grams of copper, 3.003 grams of carbon, or 1.008 grams of hydrogen would serve the purpose. This weight of an element which combines with 8 grams of oxygen is given *a special name. It is called the equivalent weight of the element.*

Illustrative Problems

1. If 4.08 g. of zinc combine with 1 g. of oxygen, what is the equivalent weight of zinc?

Solution. By definition, the equivalent weight of zinc is that weight of the element, in grams, which combines with 8 g. of oxygen.

Weight of zinc that combines with 8 g. of oxygen

$$= 8 \times \text{wt. that combines with 1 g. of oxygen}$$
$$= 8 \times 4.08 \text{ g.} = 32.64 \qquad Ans. \ 32.64.$$

* Some authors use the term "combining weight" instead of equivalent weight.

† The reason 8 g. of oxygen was chosen is that with a smaller weight of oxygen, the weight of hydrogen would be less than 1 g. We wish to avoid numbers smaller than unity.

2. If 1.2500 g. of an oxide of iron contains 0.8742 g. of iron, calculate the equivalent weight of iron.

Solution. If there are 0.8742 g. of iron in 1.2500 g. of oxide, there must be 1.2500 − 0.8742 = 0.3758 g. of oxygen. (Since the oxide contains only oxygen and iron.) Now we wish to find the weight of iron per 8 g. of oxygen.

Wt. of iron per 8 g. of oxygen = 8 × Wt. of iron per gram of oxygen

$$= 8 \times \frac{0.8742}{0.3758} = 18.61 \text{ g.} \quad Ans. \ 18.61.$$

3. The equivalent weight of iron is 18.61, what weight of iron will combine with 6 g. of oxygen?

Solution.

Wt. combining with 1 g. of oxygen

$$= \frac{\text{Wt. combining with 8 g. of oxygen}}{8}$$

$$= \frac{18.61}{8} \text{ g.}$$

Wt. combining with 6 g. of oxygen

$$= 6 \times \text{Wt. combining with 1 g. oxygen}$$

$$= 6 \times \frac{18.61}{8} \text{ g.} = 13.96 \text{ g.} \quad Ans. \ 13.96 \text{ g.}$$

Problems

1. One gram of the metal aluminum combines with 0.89 g. of oxygen. What is the equivalent weight of aluminum?   *Ans.* 9.0.

2. The equivalent weight of zinc is 32.69. What weight of zinc will combine with 3.2 g. of oxygen?

3. If 10.79 g. of silver combines with oxygen to form 11.59 g. of oxide, what is the equivalent weight of silver?

Some elements will not combine directly with oxygen. How then can their equivalent weights be obtained? We have just learned that 1.008 grams of hydrogen (its equivalent weight) combines with 8 grams of oxygen; therefore 1.008 grams of hydrogen is chemically equivalent to 8 g. of oxygen. If an element combines with hydrogen, to find the equivalent weight of the element it is necessary only to find the weight of it, in grams, that combines with 1.008 grams of hydrogen. We may generalize our definition of equivalent weights then and say: *The equivalent weight of an element is that weight of the element, in grams, which combines with one equivalent weight of another element, the equivalent weight of oxygen being taken as 8 grams.*

Illustrative Problem

The element bromine does not combine readily with oxygen; it does, however, combine with silver. 11.272 g. of bromine combines with 15.215 g. of silver. The equivalent weight of silver is 107.88. Calculate the equivalent weight of bromine.

Solution. The equivalent weight of bromine is that weight in grams that combines with one equivalent weight, 107.88 g., of silver = 107.88 $\times$ wt. of bromine combining with 1 g. of silver = $107.88 \times \dfrac{11.272}{15.215} =$ 79.923 g. *Ans.* 79.923.

Problems

1. If 4.1 g. of zinc combines with 1 g. of oxygen and 65.4 g. of zinc combines with 71 g. of chlorine, what is the equivalent weight of chlorine?

2. Using the equivalent weight of chlorine obtained in problem 1, calculate the weight of chlorine that will combine with 1 g. of hydrogen.

If each of the ninety-two elements had only one equivalent weight, we could calculate the weight of an element that would combine with a given weight of any other element. But some of the elements have more than one equivalent weight. Carbon and iron have two each, arsenic has three, and nitrogen has five equivalent weights. Therefore, to calculate the weight of nitrogen that will combine with a given weight of some other element, we must know which of the equivalent weights to use in the given problem.

There is a property of the elements, however, which, unlike the equivalent weight, does not vary. It is the atomic weight and is related to the equivalent weight by the relation,

$$\text{Atomic weight} = \text{Equivalent weight} \times \text{Valence} \qquad (1)$$

This leads us to two new and important topics—atomic weights and valence. These will be discussed later (Chapters VI and VII).

3. The five equivalent weights of nitrogen are: 2.8, 3.5, 4.66, 7, and 14.

(a) Are these equivalent weights related to one another in any simple way?

(b) When the equivalent weight of nitrogen is 14, its valence is 1. What is the atomic weight of nitrogen?

(c) What is the valence of nitrogen corresponding to each of the other four equivalent weights?

4. The oxide of zinc contains 19.7 per cent oxygen. What is the equivalent weight of zinc?   *Ans.* 32.6.

5. Calculate the equivalent weight of iron in the oxide which contains 70 per cent iron.

6. The equivalent weight of sodium is 23. Calculate the percentage of sodium in its oxide.

7. A certain oxide has the formula Fe_2O_3. Using a table of atomic weights, calculate the equivalent weight of iron in this oxide.

8. A 13.5-g. sample of a tin oxide was found to contain 11.9 g. of tin. What is the equivalent weight of tin in this oxide?

9. Calculate the equivalent weight of copper in the oxide CuO.

10. The atomic weight of magnesium is less than that of aluminum but the equivalent weight of magnesium is more than that of aluminum. Explain.

11. Calcium oxide is 71.43 per cent calcium. What is the equivalent weight of calcium?

12. The density of calcium is 1.5 g/cc. What is the volume of an equivalent weight of calcium? (See problem 11.)

13. The density of iron is 7.9 g/cc. Is an equivalent weight of iron larger by volume than an equivalent weight of calcium? (See problems above.)

14. Silver has an equivalent weight of 107.9. Calculate the percentage of silver in its oxide.

CHAPTER III

PERCENTAGE COMPOSITION, MOLECULAR FORMULAS

As you know, the formula of a compound expresses the number of atoms of each of the elements in one molecule of the compound. The compound carbon dioxide has the formula CO_2. This formula tells us that two atoms of oxygen are combined with one atom of carbon to form one molecule of carbon dioxide. Now the problem is: If the formula of a compound is known, can the percentage composition of the compound be calculated? (By percentage composition, we mean the percentage by weight of each element in the compound.) To illustrate this calculation, we shall use carbon dioxide as an example. We wish to find the percentage composition of carbon dioxide.

By definition,

$$\text{Per cent carbon} = \frac{\text{Wt. carbon}}{\text{Total wt.}} \times 100$$

and

$$\text{Per cent oxygen} = \frac{\text{Wt. of oxygen}}{\text{Total wt.}} \times 100$$

The atomic weight of carbon is 12.01 and that of oxygen is 16.00. The molecular weight of carbon dioxide is 44.01 (12.01 parts carbon and 32.00 parts oxygen). Then

$$\text{Per cent carbon} = \frac{12.01}{44.01} \times 100 = 27.29$$

$$\text{Per cent oxygen} = \frac{32.00}{44.01} \times 100 = 72.71$$

Notice that the sum of the individual percentages is 100. This serves as a check on the work.

Problems

1. What is the percentage composition of water, H_2O?

Ans. Oxygen 88.8%, hydrogen 11.2%.

2. What is the percentage composition of hydrogen sulfate, H_2SO_4?

Ans. 2.05% hydrogen, 32.69% sulfur, 65.26% oxygen.

3. If a basket of fruit contains 6 apples, 4 oranges, and 10 peaches, what is its percentage composition?

4. What is the percentage composition of $KClO_3$, potassium chlorate?

5. If one molecular weight of a certain compound contains 32 parts sulfur and is 94.1 per cent sulfur, what is the molecular weight of the compound?

MOLECULAR FORMULA FROM PERCENTAGE COMPOSITION

Actually, the calculation of the percentage composition of a compound from its molecular formula is not an important one. However, the reverse, i.e., the calculation of the molecular formula of a compound from its percentage composition, is very important. It is a relatively easy matter to determine the percentage composition of a compound by laboratory experiment. For example, if one wished to obtain the percentage composition of water, he could decompose a given weight of it into its constituents, hydrogen and oxygen, and from the weights of these calculate thus,

$$\text{Per cent oxygen} = \frac{\text{Wt. of oxygen}}{\text{Wt. of water}} \times 100$$

$$\text{Per cent hydrogen} = \frac{\text{Wt. of hydrogen}}{\text{Wt. of water}} \times 100$$

He would find water to be 88.8 per cent oxygen and 11.2 per cent hydrogen. Now the question is: Can the formula of water be obtained from its percentage composition alone, or is more information necessary? (Before going further, attempt to calculate the formula for water from its percentage composition.) Remember that we are attempting to find the number of atoms of oxygen and the number of atoms of hydrogen in one molecule of water.

1. Determination of the ratio of hydrogen atoms to oxygen atoms in a molecule of water.

Solution. We know that there are 11.2 parts of hydrogen and 88.8 parts of oxygen in 100 parts of water. One atom of oxygen weighs 16.0, and one atom of hydrogen weighs 1.008. Then, the relative number of hydrogen atoms in 11.2 parts of hydrogen = $\frac{11.2}{1.008}$ = 11.1, and the relative number of oxygen atoms in 88.8 parts of oxygen = $\frac{88.8}{16.0}$ = 5.56. Thus, there are 11.1 atoms of hydrogen for every 5.56 atoms of oxygen in water.

2. What is the simplest formula for water?

Solution. From the above we might write water as $H_{11.1}O_{5.56}$. This formula gives the correct composition of water, but molecules are made up of whole atoms. Since 11.1 is approximately 2×5.56 we see that the simplest possible formula is H_2O.

3. What is the correct molecular formula for water and what information, other than the percentage composition, is necessary for calculating it?

Solution. From the simplest formula we cannot know whether the correct formula for water is H_2O, H_4O_2, H_6O_3, $H_{100}O_{50}$ or in general $H_{2n}O_n$ (where n is any whole number). If we know the molecular weight in addition to the percentage composition we can determine the true formula in either of two ways.

A. (1) Determine the simplest formula as we did above.
   (2) Determine what multiple of the molecular weight as calculated from the simplest formula corresponds to the known molecular weight.

In the foregoing, from the percentage composition, we found that there are twice as many hydrogen atoms in water as oxygen. Then the simplest formula is H_2O. The molecular weight as calculated from the simplest formula is 2 times atomic weight of hydrogen plus $1 \times$ atomic weight of oxygen, or $2 \times 1.008 + 16.000 = 18.016$. The molecular weight of water is actually found to be 18.016. Thus the simplest formula for water is also its true formula.

B. When both the percentage composition and the molecular

weight are known, there is a much simpler and more direct way of finding the true formula.

(1) Calculate the weight of each element in a molecular weight. Thus,

Wt. of hydrogen in 1 mol. wt. $H_2O = 18.016 \times 0.112 = 2.02$

Wt. of oxygen in 1 mol. wt. $H_2O = 18.016 \times 0.888 = 16.00$

(2) Find the number of atoms of each element in a molecule by dividing the weight of that element in a molecule by its atomic weight.

Therefore,

$$\text{Atoms of hydrogen in 1 molecule } H_2O = \frac{2.02}{1.008} = 2$$

$$\text{Atoms of oxygen in 1 molecule } H_2O = \frac{16.00}{16.00} = 1$$

Thus the formula for water is H_2O.

Illustrative Problems

1. An analysis of alcohol shows it to be 52.12 per cent carbon, 13.13 per cent hydrogen, and 34.74 per cent oxygen.

(a) Find the relative number of atoms of each element in alcohol and express its simplest formula.

Solution. From the definition of percentage it follows that in 100 parts of alcohol there are 52.12 parts of carbon, 13.13 parts of hydrogen, and 34.74 parts of oxygen. Thus we have the relative weights of the three elements in the compound. But what we wish to find is the relative number of atoms.

Since one carbon atom weighs 12.01, in 52.12 parts of carbon there are $\frac{52.12}{12.01} = 4.34$ atoms of carbon. Since the atomic weight of hydrogen is 1.008, in 13.13 parts of hydrogen there are $\frac{13.13}{1.008} = 13.02$ atoms of hydrogen; and, similarly, since the atomic weight of oxygen is 16.00, there are in 34.74 parts of oxygen $\frac{34.74}{16.00} = 2.17$ atoms of oxygen.

The relative number of atoms of the three elements in alcohol is 4.34 atoms of carbon to 13.02 atoms of hydrogen to 2.17 atoms of oxygen.

And in so far as weights are concerned, the formula for alcohol might be $C_{4.34}H_{13.02}O_{2.17}$. This formula satisfies the percentage composition, but we know that this cannot be the true formula since fractional atoms do not exist in chemical compounds. Now there are fewer oxygen atoms than carbon or hydrogen atoms in the molecule, so let us suppose there is only one atom of oxygen in a molecule of alcohol. Then there are $\dfrac{4.34}{2.17} = 2$ atoms of carbon and $\dfrac{13.02}{2.17} = 6$ atoms of hydrogen, and the formula is C_2H_6O. Is this a possible formula? Yes, since it satisfies the percentage composition and also contains only whole numbers of atoms. Is it the simplest possible formula for alcohol? Yes, because a simpler formula would contain less than one atom of oxygen, and this is impossible. Might not the formula, however, be $C_4H_{12}O_2$ or $C_6H_{18}O_3$? Yes, these are possible. What further information is necessary in order to decide which of these possible formulas is the correct one? The answer is: the molecular weight.

(b) If the molecular weight of alcohol is 46, what is its true molecular formula?

Solution. The formula $C_4H_{12}O_2$ corresponds to a molecular weight of 92 (48 for carbon, 12 for hydrogen, and 32 for oxygen). The formula C_2H_6O corresponds to a molecular weight of 46 (24 for carbon, 6 for hydrogen, and 16 for oxygen); therefore, this is the molecular formula.

In working a problem of this type it is well to summarize your work in a table, thus:

ELEMENTS	%	PARTS IN 100 PARTS	RELATIVE NUMBER OF ATOMS	RELATIVE NUMBER ATOMS AS WHOLE NUMBERS	SIMPLEST FORMULA
Carbon	52.12	52.12	$\dfrac{52.12}{12.01} = 4.34$	2	
Hydrogen	13.13	13.13	$\dfrac{13.13}{1.008} = 13.02$	6	C_2H_6O
Oxygen	34.74	34.74	$\dfrac{34.74}{16.00} = 2.17$	1	

2. An oxide of tin contains 23.7 g. of tin combined with 6.4 g. of oxygen. What is the simplest formula of this oxide?

ELEMENTS	PARTS BY WEIGHT	RELATIVE NUMBER ATOMS	RELATIVE NUMBER ATOMS IN WHOLE NUMBERS	SIMPLEST FORMULA
Tin	23.7	$\dfrac{23.7}{119} = 0.2$	1	
Oxygen	6.4	$\dfrac{6.4}{16} = 0.4$	2	SnO_2

Problems

1. Mercuric oxide contains 92.61 per cent Hg and 7.39 per cent oxygen. What is its simplest formula? *Ans.* HgO.

2. Experiments prove the compound potassium chlorate to have the following composition: K = 31.9 per cent, Cl = 28.9 per cent, and O = 39.2 per cent. What is the simplest formula? *Ans.* $KClO_3$.

3. A farmer shipped to market a carload of livestock consisting of cows, hogs, and sheep. Each cow weighed 700 lb., each hog 400 lb., and each sheep 150 lb. The cows made up 49 per cent, the hogs 36 per cent, and the sheep 15 per cent of the total weight.

(a) Were there more cows, hogs, or sheep in the car? *Ans.* Sheep.

(b) What was the relative number of each?
Ans. 7 cows to 9 hogs to 10 sheep.

(c) If the combined weight of the animals was 10 tons, what was the actual number of each?
Ans. 14 cows, 18 hogs, and 20 sheep.

4. What is the simplest formula of a substance which gives on analysis: 27.93 per cent iron, 24.05 per cent sulfur, and 48.02 per cent oxygen?
Ans. $Fe_2S_3O_{12}$.

5. Analysis shows a certain compound to consist of 47.48 per cent sulfur and 52.52 per cent chlorine. Its molecular weight is 133. What is (a) its simplest formula, and (b) its true formula?
Ans. (a) SCl, (b) S_2Cl_2.

6. A certain compound is 92.25 per cent carbon and 7.75 per cent hydrogen. Its molecular weight is 78. What is its true molecular formula?

7. What is the simplest formula of a compound of carbon and hydrogen containing 75 per cent carbon?

8. Quicklime is 71.4 per cent calcium and 28.6 per cent oxygen. Its molecular weight is 56. What is its formula?

9. A certain compound contains 32.4 per cent sodium, 22.5 per cent sulfur, and 45.1 per cent oxygen. What is its simplest formula?

10. Urea is 46.67 per cent nitrogen, 20.00 per cent carbon, 6.67 per cent hydrogen, and 26.67 per cent oxygen. What is its simplest formula? Its molecular weight is 60. What is its true formula?

11. A certain organic compound contains 26.67 per cent carbon, 71.09 per cent oxygen, and 2.24 per cent hydrogen. Its molecular weight is 90.0. What is its formula?

CHAPTER IV

THE GAS LAWS

We learned in Chapter I that the volume occupied by a gas is very sensitive to changes in pressure and temperature. Increasing pressure tends to decrease the volume, and increasing temperature tends to increase the volume of a given weight of gas. This is a matter of common experience. The question we wish to consider is, what is the quantitative relationship between these variables—the volume, pressure, and temperature of a gas? That is, if we are given the volume of a certain weight of gas at some temperature and pressure, how can we calculate what the volume will be at some other temperature and pressure?

THE EFFECT OF A CHANGE IN PRESSURE

In 1660, Boyle discovered the relation between the volume and pressure of a gas at constant temperature. He discovered this relation *experimentally* in the following way: He placed a convenient amount of air in such an apparatus that the volume occupied by the gas and the pressure exerted on it (by a column of mercury) could be easily observed. He obtained results similar to the following, where V and P represent volume in cubic centimeters and pressure in millimeters of mercury.

V	P
1900	200
1000	380
500	760
250	1520
100	3800

Now, qualitatively, we see that as P increases, V decreases. But we want the quantitative relation between P and V, by use of which V can be calculated for any given P. Notice that the product of P times the corresponding V gives the same figure, 380,000, each time. P times V is, therefore, constant.

$$P \times V = K * \quad \text{Temperature constant} \tag{1}$$

or

$$V = \frac{K}{P}$$

This relation is given in words by Boyle's law: For a given sample of gas at constant temperature, the volume varies inversely with the pressure.

The law is sometimes written in the form,

$$PV = P'V' \tag{2}$$

Equation 2, of course, follows from the fact that for a given sample of gas the product of its V and its corresponding P equals the same K: thus

$$P \times V = K \quad \text{and} \quad P'V' = K$$

and since two things equal to the same thing equal each other,

$$PV = P'V'$$

Thus, if for a given sample of gas at a given temperature, we know the volume corresponding to a given pressure, we can calculate the volume at any other pressure, by equation 2 in the form,

$$V' = V \times \frac{P}{P'} \tag{3}$$

Notice, by equation 3, that the new volume V' is equal to the old volume V multiplied by a pressure factor $\frac{P}{P'}$. In order to avoid error in using the pressure factor, it is necessary only to glance back to the problem and ascertain whether the pressure increased or decreased. If it increased, the new volume must be less than the old; whereas if it decreased, the new volume must be greater than the old.

* The numerical value of this constant is determined by the amount of gas used and by the temperature.

THE EFFECT OF A CHANGE IN TEMPERATURE

Many years after the time of Boyle (1660), two men, Charles and Gay-Lussac (1805), working independently, discovered the effect of a change in temperature, at constant pressure, on the volume of a gas. It is a matter of common experience that the volume of a gas, at constant pressure, increases with increasing temperatures. But in what quantitative way? Both Charles and Gay-Lussac observed that if a given amount of gas is heated at constant pressure, from 0° C. to 273° C., its volume is doubled. The relation between the volume of a gas and the temperature on the centigrade scale is not a very simple one, since by *adding* 273° to 0° C., we *multiplied* the volume by two. Rather than express such a relation, Charles and Gay-Lussac decided to define a new temperature scale such that the temperature, as measured on this scale, is directly proportional to the volume of a given sample of gas. Thus 0° C., as expressed on the new scale, must be one-half of 273° C., as expressed on the new scale (since the volume is one-half as large). Obviously then, the new scale, called the absolute scale, is obtained from the centigrade scale by adding 273° to the centigrade scale.* Thus 0° C. = 273° Absolute (A.), and 273° C. = 273° + 273° = 546° A.

Charles' or Gay-Lussac's law can be stated in words: The volume of a given sample of gas, at constant pressure, is directly proportional to the *absolute* temperature. Letting T represent the absolute temperature, we can express the law in symbols thus:

$$V = KT$$

$$\frac{V}{T} = K \tag{4}$$

This equation 4 tells us that if we take a sample of gas, at some pressure, the fraction obtained by dividing the absolute temperature into the volume will remain unchanged, no matter how the

---

* This result can be obtained algebraically in this way: Let X equal the number of degrees to be added to the centigrade scale to obtain the absolute scale; then 0° C. = X° A., and 273° C. = (273° + X°) A. Now the condition on this new scale is that the temperature, as expressed on this scale, be directly proportional to the volume; therefore,

$$2X = 273° + X$$

$$X = 273°$$

volume or the temperature is changed. If the temperature is reduced to one-tenth of its original value, the volume will be reduced to one-tenth of its original value. In general, at some new temperature T' this same amount of gas will occupy a new volume V'. Then

$$\frac{V'}{T'} = K \tag{5}$$

But two things equal to the same thing are equal to each other; therefore from (4) and (5) we obtain

$$\frac{V}{T} = \frac{V'}{T'}$$

or

$$V' = V \times \frac{T'}{T} \tag{6}$$

By use of equation 6, one can calculate the volume of a given sample of gas at any temperature knowing the volume at some other temperature, provided the pressure has not changed. To avoid the possible error in using the temperature factor, it is necessary only to remember that increasing the temperature tends to increase the volume.

THE EFFECT OF CHANGES IN BOTH TEMPERATURE AND PRESSURE

We are now confronted with this problem: Knowing the volume of a given sample of gas at some temperature and pressure, calculate the volume at some other temperature and pressure.

Obviously, we can accomplish this by first changing the pressure while keeping the temperature constant, i.e., by using equation 3 and then changing the temperature while keeping the pressure constant, i.e., by using equation 6. Thus, if we know the volume V, at temperature T, and the pressure P, and wish to find the volume V', at temperature T' and pressure P', we can first change the pressure to P', keeping the temperature at T. The volume will change to a new value, which we shall call V_1. By equation 3

$$V_1 = V \frac{P}{P'} \tag{7}$$

We shall now change the temperature to T', keeping the pressure at P'; the volume will change from V_1 up to V', and by equation 6

$$V' = V_1 \frac{T'}{T} \quad \text{or} \quad V_1 = V' \frac{T}{T'} \tag{8}$$

This gives us our desired result, V'. But is it not possible to calculate V' directly without first calculating V_1; that is to say, is there not a direct relation between V, P, T, V', P', and T' such that if five of these six variables are known, the other may be calculated?

Such a relation can be obtained by eliminating V_1 between equations 7 and 8. Doing this, we obtain the expression

$$V' \frac{T}{T'} = V \frac{P}{P'} \tag{9}$$

On rearranging this we obtain the general gas law

$$\frac{PV}{T} = \frac{P'V'}{T'} \tag{10}$$

or

$$V' = V \times \frac{T'}{T} \times \frac{P}{P'} \tag{11}$$

Now to solve problems of this type you need not even remember equation 10; you need only remember that the new volume V' is equal to the old volume V multiplied by a temperature factor and by a pressure factor. From the law predict how the temperature change will affect the volume and similarly predict how the pressure change will affect the volume. Now set up each factor to produce these predicted results.

STANDARD CONDITIONS

As we have seen, the density of a gas (the weight per liter) is quite dependent on the conditions of temperature and pressure. If densities of different gases are to be compared and if the comparison is to have any meaning, it is necessary that these densities correspond to the same conditions of temperature and pressure. It is universally agreed that by the density of a gas we mean the density at 0° C. (273° A.) and 760 mm. pressure unless, of course, other conditions are explicitly stated. These conditions of temperature and pressure, 0° C. and 760 mm., are called *standard conditions* and are abbreviated S.T.P. (for *S*tandard *T*emperature and *P*ressure).

DALTON'S LAW OF PARTIAL PRESSURES

Often gases are collected over water or some other liquid. When this is done, the container in which the gas is collected will contain, besides the gas, some vapor of the water or other liquid. Vapors are gases and act like gases in regard to change in temperature and pressure.

Consider this problem: If a container of volume V is filled with a gas collected over water at a temperature T and barometric pressure P, what will be the volume of this gas when dry at temperature T' and pressure P'? We cannot use equation 11 because the original pressure P is not the pressure of the gas alone but that of the gas plus that of the water vapor. Suppose we know the pressure of the water vapor, could we calculate the pressure of the gas alone? Yes, by use of Dalton's law of partial pressures: *The total pressure exerted by a mixture of gases is equal to the sum of the pressures which each would exert if it alone occupied the whole space.* Or, in symbols,

$$P_{\text{total}} = P_{\text{gas}} + P_{\text{water vapor}}$$

Therefore,

$$P_{\text{gas}} = P_{\text{total}} - P_{\text{water vapor}} \qquad (12)$$

If the pressure of the water vapor is known and the barometric pressure is also known, P_{gas} can be calculated by equation 12; and then equation 11 can be used to complete the calculation. Or we can take these two steps in one, for by substituting equation 12 into equation 11, we get

$$V' = V \times \frac{T'}{T} \times \frac{P_{\text{total}} - P_{\text{H}_2\text{O}}}{P'} \qquad (13)$$

where V' is the final volume of the dry gas at P' and T'. T is the original temperature and V the original volume of the wet gas. P_{total} is the barometric pressure at which the wet gas was collected, and $P_{\text{H}_2\text{O}}$ the pressure of the water vapor. Again, equation 13 need not be memorized, in fact, should not be memorized; by our common sense method we can determine what should go into the numerator and what into the denominator of our factors.

VAPOR PRESSURE OF WATER IN MILLIMETERS OF MERCURY

°C.	P	°C.	P	°C.	P	°C.	P	°C.	P
11	9.8	16	13.5	21	18.5	26	25.0	31	33.4
12	10.4	17	14.4	22	19.6	27	26.5	32	35.3
13	11.1	18	15.3	23	20.9	28	28.1	33	37.4
14	11.9	19	16.3	24	22.2	29	29.7	34	39.5
15	12.7	20	17.4	25	23.5	30	31.5	35	41.8

Illustrative Problems

1. A sample of oxygen which occupies 3.0 l. at 760 mm. pressure will occupy what volume at 190 mm., the temperature remaining constant?

Solution. From Boyle's law, we know that the new volume, which we shall call V, is equal to the old volume multiplied by a pressure factor consisting of one of the pressures divided by the other. It is only a question of which pressure is to be the numerator and which the denominator of the factor. The pressure is decreased; therefore, the volume will increase. Then the pressure factor is greater than 1, so the larger pressure 760 must be in the numerator. Then

$$V = 3.0 \times \frac{760}{190} = 12 \text{ l.} \qquad\qquad Ans. \text{ 12 l.}$$

2. The 12 l. of oxygen obtained in (1) is heated at constant pressure from 0° to 91° C. What is the new volume?

Solution. Recalling Gay-Lussac's law and obtaining our temperature factor by a reasoning process similar to that used in (1), we get, after changing to absolute temperature,

$$V = 12 \times \frac{364}{273} = 16 \text{ l.} \qquad\qquad Ans. \text{ 16 l.}$$

3. A 3.0-l. sample of oxygen at standard conditions will occupy what volume at 91° C. and 190 mm.? (This problem is the same as 1 and 2 combined. Be sure you understand this fact before proceeding.)

Solution. By the general gas law, the new volume is equal to the old volume multiplied by a pressure factor, which in this case is greater than

1, since the pressure is decreased, and by a temperature factor, which also is greater than one, since the temperature is increased. Then

$$V = 3.0 \times \frac{760}{190} \times \frac{364}{273} = 16 \text{ l.} \qquad Ans. \ 16 \text{ l.}$$

4. A sample of gas collected over water at 22° C. and a barometric pressure of 730 mm. occupies 850 cc. What volume will this gas occupy dry at standard conditions? The vapor pressure of water at 22° C. is 20 mm.

Solution. This problem is similar to problem 3, except that we are not given the original pressure of the gas alone. But this can be calculated very simply by Dalton's law of partial pressure, according to which,

$$P_{\text{total}} = P_{\text{gas}} + P_{\text{water}}$$

$$P_{\text{gas}} = P_{\text{total}} - P_{\text{water}} = 730 - 20 = 710 \text{ mm.}$$

Now we can restate our problem in this way: 850 cc. of a gas at 710 mm. and 22° C. will occupy what volume at standard conditions?

Using the general gas law as in problem 3, we obtain

$$V = 850 \times \frac{273}{295} \times \frac{710}{760} = 735 \text{ cc.}$$

The problem could, of course, be solved in one step by equation 13; thus

$$V = 850 \times \frac{273}{295} \times \frac{730 - 20}{760} = 735 \text{ cc.}$$

Problems

1. A volume of helium measuring 600 cc. at a pressure of 735.5 mm. is subjected to a pressure of 800 mm. What is the new volume?

Ans. 552 cc.

2. A sample of gas occupies 350 cc. at 20° C. What volume will it occupy at −10° C., if the pressure is not changed? *Ans.* 314 cc.

3. If 100 cc. of a gas at 15° C. is heated to a temperature of 30° C., the pressure remaining constant, what is the new volume? *Ans.* 105 cc.

4. A liter of hydrogen at 0° C. and 760 mm. pressure is subjected to a pressure of 20 atm. (an atm. is 760 mm. of mercury) and a temperature of 20° C. Calculate the new volume. *Ans.* 53.7 cc.

5. A sample of gas occupying a volume of 300 cc. at 20° C. exerts a pressure of 700 mm. What will be the volume of this gas at 35° C. and 600 mm.?

6. If 500 cc. of hydrogen is collected over water at 26° C. and a barometric pressure of 725 mm., what volume will it occupy dry at S.T.P.?

7. (*a*) At constant pressure what is the relation between the density of a gas and the absolute temperature? (*b*) What is the relation between the density, temperature, and pressure of a gas?

8. The density of nitrogen at standard conditions is 1.25 g/l. What is the density of nitrogen at 21° C. and 750 mm. pressure? *Ans.* 1.15 g/l.

9. The density of oxygen at S.T.P. is 1.429 g/l. If 200 cc. at S.T.P. is compressed at constant temperature until its volume is 130 cc., calculate the weight of 30 cc. of the compressed gas. *Ans.* 0.066 g.

10. A quantity of gas weighing 9.0 g. at 350 mm. pressure and −150° C. is heated to 300° C. and the pressure changed to 300 mm. If 500 cc. of this rarified gas weighs 1.0 g., calculate the original volume of the gas.

11. One liter of dry nitrogen at S.T.P. is bubbled through water and collected at 25° C. and a barometric pressure of 750 mm. What is the volume of this wet gas?

12. A sample of oxygen collected over water at 25° C. and 740 mm. total pressure measures 200 cc.

(*a*) If this gas is dried, what will be its volume at 25° C. and 700 mm.?

(*b*) If this gas is not dried, what will be its volume at 25° C. and 700 mm.?

CHAPTER V

PROBLEMS BASED ON CHEMICAL EQUATIONS *

We have already learned that a chemical equation is a shorthand method of expressing certain information about a chemical reaction by the use of symbols and formulas which if expressed in words would require much more space. For example, the equation

$$2KClO_3 = 2KCl + 3O_2$$

tells us the following.

(a) Potassium chlorate decomposes to give potassium chloride and oxygen.

(b) Two molecules of potassium chlorate yield 2 molecules of potassium chloride and 3 molecules of oxygen.

(c) Knowing that the molecular weight of potassium chlorate is 122.6, the molecular weight of potassium chloride is 74.6, and the molecular weight of oxygen is 32, we know that

$$2 \times 122.6 \text{ g. } KClO_3 \text{ yield } 2 \times 74.6 \text{ g. } KCl + 3 \times 32 \text{ g. } O_2$$

It should again be pointed out that all chemical equations, to be correct, must obey the law of conservation of matter. In other words, the total number of atoms of any element must be the same on each side of the equation. Since this is true, the total weight of the substances reacting must always be equal to the total weight of the substances formed.

The application of this information to the solution of problems is illustrated below.

Illustrative Problems

1. How many grams of oxygen can be obtained by heating 490 g. of potassium chlorate? The equation for the reaction is:

$$2KClO_3 = 2KCl + 3O_2$$

* This chapter may be omitted and pages 69–74 be used instead.

Solution. This equation tells us that 2 molecules of $KClO_3$ give 3 molecules of O_2. The molecular weight of $KClO_3 = 39.1 + 35.5 + (3 \times 16) = 122.6$, and the molecular weight of oxygen $= 2 \times 16 = 32$. We now see that 2×122.6 g. $KClO_3$ will give 3×32 g. O_2.

1 g. $KClO_3$ will yield $\dfrac{3 \times 32}{2 \times 122.6}$ g. O_2.

490 g. $KClO_3$ will yield $\dfrac{3 \times 32}{2 \times 122.6} \times 490$ g. $O_2 = 192$ g. O_2 *Ans.*

2. What weight of zinc is needed to displace 18 g. of hydrogen from sulfuric acid? The equation for the reaction is:

$$Zn + H_2SO_4 = ZnSO_4 + H_2$$

Solution. One atom of zinc displaces 1 molecule of hydrogen. The atomic weight of zinc is 65, and the molecular weight of hydrogen is 2×1.0 or 2.0. Then,

65 g. of Zn displaces 2.0 g. of H_2

or

2.0 g. of H_2 requires 65 g. of Zn

1.0 g. of H_2 requires $\dfrac{65}{2.0}$ g. of Zn

18 g. of H_2 requires $\dfrac{65}{2.0} \times 18 = 585$ g. of Zn   *Ans.*

The reasoning involved in these problems is exactly the same as would be used in buying apples from the grocer.

3. Apples are selling for 30 cents per dozen. How many apples can be purchased for 75 cents?

Solution.

30 cents will buy 12 apples

1 cent will buy $\dfrac{12}{30}$ apples

75 cents will buy $\dfrac{12}{30} \times 75 = 30$ apples

Problems

1. What weight of mercuric oxide is required to prepare 24.0 g. of oxygen?   *Ans.* 325 g.

2. Sufficient potassium chlorate is decomposed to give 5.6 g. of oxygen. What weight of potassium chloride is formed?   *Ans.* 8.7 g.

3. What weight of hydrogen sulfate is required to react with 325 g. of zinc?   *Ans.* 490 g.

4. A mixture containing potassium chlorate and manganese dioxide weighed 5.00 g. It was heated until all the oxygen from the potassium chlorate had been liberated. The resulting mixture weighed 4.00 g. (*a*) What was the weight of the potassium chlorate in the mixture? (*b*) What was the percentage of manganese dioxide in the mixture?

Ans. (*a*) 2.55 g.   (*b*) 49.0%.

5. Sulfuric acid can be made from iron pyrite, FeS_2, as shown by the equations below.

$$4FeS_2 + 11O_2 = 2Fe_2O_3 + 8SO_2$$

$$2SO_2 + O_2 = 2SO_3$$

$$SO_3 + H_2O = H_2SO_4$$

What weight of sulfuric acid can be obtained from 10.0 kg. of FeS_2?

6. Methane, CH_4, burns to yield carbon dioxide and water. (*a*) What weight of oxygen is needed for the combustion of 48.0 g. of methane? (*b*) If air is 23 per cent oxygen by weight, what weight of air is needed?

Ans. (*a*) 192 g.   (*b*) 835 g.

7. A sample of sodium is 75 per cent pure. What weight of hydrogen can be prepared by the action of 100 g. of this impure sodium on water?

8. A sample of potassium chlorate is found to be 90 per cent pure. What weight of this potassium chlorate is needed to prepare 50 g. of oxygen?

9. What weight of hydrogen will be displaced from hydrochloric acid by 100 g. of zinc?

10. What weight of zinc is needed to displace 2.0 g. of hydrogen from hydrochloric acid?

11. What weight of magnesium will displace from an acid the same amount of hydrogen as is displaced by 16 g. of zinc?

12. Which would liberate the greater amount of hydrogen from an acid—10 g. of zinc or 10 g. of magnesium? Give reasons.

13. How much pure silver must be dissolved in nitric acid to form 150.0 g. of $AgNO_3$?

CHAPTER VI

VALENCE

The valence of an atom is a number which indicates how many atoms of hydrogen or chlorine one atom of the element will hold or displace.* Since gram-atomic weights of all elements contain the same number of atoms, we can state the definition in terms of gram-atomic weights. *The valence of a given element is the number of gram-atomic weights of hydrogen or chlorine one gram-atomic weight of the element will hold or displace.* Obviously valence is a whole number, since by the atomic theory no atom can hold in combination a fraction of a hydrogen or chlorine atom.

Many elements will be found to have two or more valences. For example, iron reacts with chlorine to form two chlorides $FeCl_2$ and $FeCl_3$. Thus the valence of iron in $FeCl_2$ is two, while it is three in $FeCl_3$.

Illustrative Problems

1. When 3.0 g. of magnesium is treated with an excess of hydrochloric acid, 0.25 g. of hydrogen is evolved. What is the valence of magnesium? *Solution.* By definition,

$$\text{Valence Mg} = \text{Number of gram-atomic weights of } H_2 \text{ displaced by 1 g-at. wt. Mg}$$

$$\text{Grams } H_2 \text{ per gram Mg} = \frac{0.25}{3.0}$$

$$\text{Grams } H_2 \text{ per gram-atomic weight Mg} = \frac{0.25}{3.0} \times 24$$

$$\text{Number of gram-atomic weight of } H_2 \text{ per gram-atomic weight Mg} = \frac{0.25}{3.0} \times \frac{24}{1.008} = 2$$

Therefore, the valence of Mg is 2.

* This definition besides being limited in scope is not strictly correct in all cases. But here we are concerned only with the simplest ideas about valence.

34

2. If 14.0 g. of a certain metal whose atomic weight is 56 gave 6.44 l. of hydrogen at 27° C. and 720 mm. when treated with sulfuric acid, what is the valence of the metal?

Solution. To find the valence is to find the number of gram-atomic weights of H_2 liberated per gram-atomic weight of the metal. There is

$$\frac{6.44}{14.0} \text{ l. of } H_2 \text{ at } 27° \text{ C. and } 720 \text{ mm. per g. of metal}$$

Therefore,

$$\frac{6.44}{14.0} \times 56.0 = 25.8 \text{ l. of } H_2 \text{ at } 27° \text{ C. and } 720 \text{ mm. per g-at. wt. of metal}$$

Now our problem is to find the number of gram-atomic weights of H_2 in this volume. Since we do not know the density of hydrogen at 27° C. and 720 mm., it is necessary to find the volume this H_2 would occupy at S.T.P.

$$V = 25.8 \times \frac{273}{300} \times \frac{720}{760} = 22.2 \text{ l.}$$

We can find the number of gram-atomic weights of H_2 in 22.2 l. by either of two methods.

(*a*) We may find the weight of the H_2 by multiplying the number of liters of H_2 by the weight of 1 l. (0.0898 g.). Thus

$$\text{Weight of } H_2 = 22.2 \times 0.0898 \text{ g.} = 2.00 \text{ g.}$$

Then,

$$\text{Number of gram-atomic weights of } H_2 \text{ per gram-atomic weight of metal} = \frac{2.00}{1.008} = 2$$

Therefore, the valence of the metal is 2.

(*b*) We know that one mole of H_2 contains 2 g-at. wts. and that it occupies 22.4 l. Therefore, 1 g-at. wt. of H_2 occupies 11.2 l. at S.T.P. Then

$$\text{Gram-atomic weights of } H_2 \text{ per gram-atomic weight of metal} = \frac{22.2}{11.2} = 2$$

Therefore, the valence of the metal is 2.

Problems

1. A 9.34-g. sample of zinc whose atomic weight is 65.38 displaces from hydrochloric acid 0.286 g. of hydrogen.

(*a*) What is the valence of the zinc? (*b*) Write the equation for the reaction.

2. If 8.00 g. of a metal whose atomic weight is 40.0 displaces 4454 cc. of hydrogen at S.T.P. from water, what is the valence of the metal?

3. The hydride of an element, whose atomic weight is 31, contains 8.82 per cent hydrogen. Calculate the valence of the element.

4. If 2.80 g. of a metal whose atomic weight is 40 reacts with chlorine to form 7.77 g. of chloride, what is the valence of the metal?

5. What is the valence of a metal 3.0 g. of which displaces 3.7 l. of H_2 from hydrochloric acid? The atomic weight of the metal is 27.

6. If 9.0 g. of a certain metal whose atomic weight is 45 displaces from sulfuric acid 14.77 l. of H_2 at 27° C. and 380 mm., what is the valence of the metal?

7. A 11.0-g. sample of a metal whose atomic weight is 63.6 combines with 12 g. of chlorine. What is the valence of the metal?

8. If 3.96 g. of tin combines with 1.50 l. of chlorine (S.T.P.), what is the valence of tin in the resulting chloride?

9. The metals nickel, magnesium, and zinc all have a valence of 2. If 6.0 g. of one of these metals displaces 0.50 g. of hydrogen from an acid, which metal is it?

10. If 12.0 g. of a metal having an atomic weight of 58.7 displaces from an acid 5.30 l. of H_2 collected over water 27° C. and 746.5 mm. barometric pressure, what is the valence of the metal?

CHAPTER VII

MOLECULAR AND ATOMIC WEIGHTS

GAY-LUSSAC'S LAW OF COMBINING VOLUMES

In 1805, Gay-Lussac found by experiment that the following is true: *In any chemical reaction the volumes of all gases concerned stand to each other in the ratio of small whole numbers.* For example, above 100° C., 2 volumes of hydrogen combine with 1 volume of oxygen to yield 2 volumes of steam (all volumes being measured under the same conditions, of course).

AVOGADRO'S LAW

On the basis of Gay-Lussac's law and Dalton's atomic theory, an Italian chemist named Avogadro offered the following law: *Equal volumes of all gases, under the same conditions of temperature and pressure, contain the same number of molecules.*

This law is of great importance in the determination of the molecular weights of gases. Remember that the molecular weight of a gas is the weight of the molecule of the gas compared with the weight of an oxygen molecule as 32. Thus, if the molecule of a certain gas is twice as heavy as the molecule of oxygen, the molecular weight of the gas is $2 \times 32 = 64$. We are unable to weigh the individual molecules because they are too small. But this is no obstacle to molecular-weight determinations, since, in order to obtain the ratio of the weights of individual molecules, it is necessary only to obtain the ratio of the weights of equal numbers of these molecules. For example, if a million nitrogen molecules weigh only $28/_{32}$ as much as a million oxygen molecules, it is obvious that one nitrogen molecule weighs only $28/_{32}$ as much as one oxygen molecule. Furthermore, if the weight of the oxygen molecule is 32, the weight of the nitrogen molecule is 28. To illustrate further with a non-chemical example, consider this: If ten Lincoln automobiles weigh twice as much as ten Fords, it is obvious that one Lincoln weighs twice as much as one Ford.

Now let us restate our problem: Having assigned to oxygen a molecular weight of 32, how can the molecular weights of other gases be determined?

The molecular weight of oxygen is 32; and, therefore, its gram-molecular weight is 32 g. Since the density of oxygen under standard conditions is 1.429 g/l., the volume occupied by one gram-molecular weight of oxygen under standard conditions is

$$V = \frac{32.0}{1.429} = 22.4 \text{ l.}$$

According to Avogadro's law, this volume, 22.4 l., at S.T.P. will contain the same number of molecules no matter what the gas. The weight of this volume of any gas will be its gram-molecular weight. Gram-molecular weight is often shortened to the single word *mole*. For this reason, the volume 22.4 liters at S.T.P. is called the *molar volume* of a gas. It is the volume occupied by one mole of gas.

Illustrative Problems

1. The density of carbon dioxide is approximately 2.0 g/l. at S.T.P. What is the molecular weight of this gas?

Solution. The gram-molecular weight is the weight in grams of 22.4 l. at S.T.P.

$$22.4 \times 2.0 = 44.8 \text{ g.}$$

The molecular weight is, therefore, 44.8.   *Ans.* 44.8.

Some of you may well wonder why we should go to this trouble to calculate the molecular weight in this way when we could very easily use the formula CO_2 and add the atomic weights to obtain a molecular weight of 44.0. Besides, 44.0 is the correct molecular weight; 44.8 is in error.

Our reply to such objection is this: You should recall that true molecular formulas can be obtained only when the molecular weight is known. It is necessary that the molecular weight be known, but it is not necessary that it be known very accurately. (Do you know why?)

2. The density of a certain gas is 1.0975 g/l. at 91° C. and 380 mm. What is the molecular weight?

Solution. We wish to find the weight of 22.4 l. at S.T.P. First, we shall calculate the volume at S.T.P. occupied by 1.0975 g. (1 l. at 91° C. and 380 mm.). One liter at 91° C. (364° A.) and 380 mm. will occupy a volume at S.T.P. of

$$V = 1000 \times \frac{273}{364} \times \frac{380}{760} = 375 \text{ cc.}$$

Wt. of 22.4 l. = 22.4 × Wt. of 1 l.

$$= 22.4 \times \frac{1.0975}{0.375} = 65.6 \text{ g.}$$

The molecular weight is, therefore, 65.6.

3. The formula of ammonia gas is NH_3. What is the density of this gas at S.T.P.?

Solution. The molecular weight of ammonia is 17.0 and its gram-molecular weight is 17.0 g. This weight of gas occupies 22.4 l. at S.T.P.; therefore,

Density at S.T.P. = Wt. of 1 l.

$$= \frac{17.0}{22.4} = 0.759 \text{ g/l.}$$

4. Calculate the number of moles in (*a*) 10 g. of oxygen, (*b*) 100 g. of H_2SO_4, and (*c*) 15.0 g. of $KClO_3$.

Solution.

(*a*) The molecular weight of oxygen is 32; therefore, one mole is 32 g. Then 10 g. $= \frac{10}{32}$ moles $= 0.31$ mole of oxygen. *Ans.*

(*b*) The molecular weight of H_2SO_4 is 98.0; therefore, one mole is 98.0 g. Then 100 g. $= \frac{100}{98.0}$ moles $= 1.02$ moles of H_2SO_4. *Ans.*

(*c*) One mole of $KClO_3$ weighs 122.6 g., since the molecular weight of $KClO_3$ is 122.6. Then 15.0 g. $= \frac{15.0}{122.6}$ mole $= 0.122$ mole of $KClO_3$. *Ans.*

Notice that the mole of a compound is one gram-molecular weight of the compound regardless of whether the compound is a gas, a liquid, or a solid.

5. What is the weight in grams of 3.56 moles of HCl?

Solution. The molecular weight of HCl is 36.5; therefore, one mole weighs 36.5 g. and 3.56 moles weighs 3.56 × 36.5 = 130 g. *Ans.*

Problems

1. A volume of gas measuring 125 cc. at 0° C. and 760 mm. pressure weighs 0.1563 g. What is the molecular weight of the gas? *Ans.* 28.0.

2. What volume will 4.00 g. of oxygen occupy at 21° C. and 705 mm. pressure? *Ans.* 3.25 l.

3. The molecular weight of a certain gas is 26.0. What is the density of this gas at 24° C. and 742 mm.? *Ans.* 1.04 g/l.

4. What is the molecular weight of a substance whose density is 1.00 g/l. at 10° C. and 1000 mm. pressure? *Ans.* 17.7.

5. What is the molecular weight of a gas, 0.182 g. of which occupies 67.0 cc. at 100° C. and 740 mm.? *Ans.* 85.4

6. A volume of gas measuring 5.65 l., collected over water at 23° C. and 755 mm. pressure, is found to weigh 6.255 g. when dry. What is the molecular weight? *Ans.* 27.8.

7. What is the molecular weight of the gas whose density is: (*a*) 1.25 g/l. at S.T.P., (*b*) 1.62 g/l. at S.T.P., and (*c*) 1.00 g/l. at 27° C. and 700 mm.?

8. What is the density of CO (*a*) at standard conditions, (*b*) at 10° C. and 700 mm. pressure?

9. When 377 cc. of a gas, collected over water at 21° C. and 747 mm. barometric pressure, is dried it weighs 0.480 g. What is the molecular weight of the gas?

10. Suppose you want 7 moles of potassium chlorate, what weight will you take?

11. Which is heavier, a mole of oxygen or a mole of nitrogen? Give your reasons.

12. Calculate the number of moles in (*a*) 75 g. of $CaCO_3$, (*b*) 15.6 g. of Na_2O_2, (*c*) 170 g. of $NaNO_3$.

13. Are there more molecules in 4 g. of oxygen or in 1 g. of hydrogen? Give reasons for your answer.

EXACT ATOMIC WEIGHTS

Until now we have been using atomic weights without showing how they are obtained. We shall now show how accurate atomic weights can be obtained.

In Chapter II it was stated:

$$\text{Exact atomic weight} = \text{Valence} \times \text{Equivalent weight} \quad (1)$$

It is a relatively easy matter to obtain the equivalent weight by a simple laboratory experiment. Then if the valence of the element corresponding to this equivalent weight is known, the atomic weight follows immediately by equation 1. In Chapter VI a method of calculating valence was discussed, but that method involved a knowledge of the atomic weight of the element. Thus we are involved in this dilemma: To obtain the atomic weight we need to know the valence, and to obtain the valence, we need to know the atomic weight. We are able to circumvent this apparent impossibility by virtue of:

1. Valence is always a whole number, and therefore accurate figures are not necessary in order to obtain an accurate value of the valence. Thus we can obtain valence from a modification of equation 1.

$$\text{Valence} = \frac{\text{Approximate atomic weight}}{\text{Equivalent weight}}$$

2. Approximate atomic weights can be obtained without a knowledge of valence. Methods of obtaining approximate atomic weights are:

(a) *For gaseous elements* approximate atomic weights can be obtained by determining experimentally the molecular weight and the number of atoms in the molecules. Then,

$$\text{Atomic weight *} = \frac{\text{Molecular weight}}{\text{Number of atoms in one molecule}}$$

For example, the density of nitrogen at S.T.P. is 1.25 g/l.; therefore, its molecular weight is $1.25 \times 22.4 = 28.0$.

Now we can find the number of atoms in the nitrogen molecule by the following steps.

(1) By experiment: 1 vol. of nitrogen + 3 vol. of hydrogen yield 2 vol. of ammonia.

(2) By Avogadro's law, the 2 vol. of ammonia contain twice as many molecules as were contained in the 1 vol. of nitrogen; i.e., each molecule of nitrogen (with hydrogen, of course) produces 2 molecules of ammonia.

(3) Every molecule of ammonia contains nitrogen, and the smallest amount it can contain is one atom. Therefore,

* Why is it difficult to obtain very accurate values of atomic weight by this method?

(4) The nitrogen molecule must contain at least two atoms. Then,

$$\text{Atomic weight} = \frac{28.0}{2} = 14.0$$

(b) *For most solid elements* the approximate atomic weights can be obtained by use of Dulong and Petit's law (1819), which states that the product of the atomic weight and the specific heat is approximately 6 calories, or

$$\text{Atomic weight} \times \text{Specific heat} = 6 *$$

This is not an exact law; the product of the specific heat of an element and its atomic weight is not always exactly 6. For example, at room temperature it is 5.8 for calcium, 5.9 for cobalt, and 6.1 for iron. But it yields with a few exceptions (especially carbon and boron) values of atomic weights which are sufficiently accurate for the determination of the valence of solid elements.

For example, the specific heat of copper is 0.0912 cal/g. By Dulong and Petit's law

$$\text{Atomic weight} = \frac{6}{0.0912} = 65.8$$

(c) *For elements that form volatile compounds* the approximate atomic weight can be obtained by following Cannizzaro's suggestions.

(1) Determine the molecular weight of the gaseous compounds of the given element. This can be done by determining the weight of 22.4 l. at S.T.P.

(2) Find by experiment the percentage of the given element in these gaseous compounds.

(3) Calculate from the results of (1) and (2) the weight of the given element in one mole of the various compounds. The smallest weight thus obtained is the atomic weight.

---

* What is the physical significance of this "constant" 6 in the Dulong-Petit law? It is the atomic heat of the element; i.e., the amount of heat required to raise the temperature of one gram-atomic weight one degree centigrade. Although the various solid elements have quite different specific heats, they all have approximately the same atomic heats.

Notice that this method is based on the assumption that at least one of the gaseous compounds contains only one atom of the given element.

As an example, consider the application of this method to the determination of the atomic weight of carbon. In the table below, the names of certain volatile carbon compounds, whose formulas are assumed to be unknown, are given in the first column. The data listed in columns 2 and 3 were determined by experiment, and the results in column 4 were calculated.

Compound	Molecular Weight	% Carbon	Weight of Carbon in One Mole of Compound
Methane	16	75	12
Ethane	30	80	24
Acetic acid	60	40	24
Methyl alcohol	32	37.5	12
Ethyl alcohol	46	52.2	24
Amyl alcohol	88	68.2	60
Ethyl ether	74	64.9	48
Benzene	78	92.3	72

From this it appears that the atomic weight of carbon is 12. The foregoing list is nowhere near complete, since there are over 300,000 known carbon compounds, but it is true that no carbon compound has been discovered containing less than 12 g. of carbon per mole of compound.

What are the sources of the inaccuracy in this method?

Once the approximate value of the atomic weight of an element has been obtained and the equivalent weight has been experimentally determined, then an accurate value of the atomic weight can be calculated in two short steps.

1.

$$\text{Valence} = \frac{\text{Approximate atomic weight}}{\text{Equivalent weight}}$$

Then,

2.

$$\text{Atomic weight} = \text{Valence} \times \text{Equivalent weight}$$

Notice that before an exact value of an atomic weight can be calculated an approximate value must be obtained.

Illustrative Problems

1. It has been found by experiment that the equivalent weight of carbon in the compound named methane is 3.0025. Using the data in the above discussion, calculate the atomic weight of carbon.

Solution. The approximate atomic weight is 12; therefore,

$$\text{Valence} = \frac{12}{3.0025} = 4$$

and

$$\text{Atomic weight} = \text{Valence} \times \text{Equivalent weight}$$

$$= 4 \times 3.0025 = 12.010. \qquad Ans. \; 12.010.$$

2. The specific heat of aluminum is 0.22 cal/g. Its equivalent weight is 8.99. What is its atomic weight?

Solution. By the Dulong and Petit law,

$$\text{Approximate atomic weight} = \frac{6}{\text{Specific heat}} = \frac{6}{0.22} = 27$$

Now we can find the valence by use of the relation:

$$\text{Atomic weight} = \text{Valence} \times \text{Equivalent weight}$$

$$27 = \text{Valence} \times 8.99$$

The problem is now: What whole number, when multiplied by 8.99, gives approximately 27? Obviously, 3. Now, discarding the approximate atomic weight 27, and using the valence, 3, we get

$$\text{Accurate atomic weight} = 3 \times 8.99 = 26.97 \quad Ans. \; 26.97.$$

Problems

1. The specific heat of the metal cadmium is 0.055 cal/g. 14.05 g. of Cd combines with 2 g. of oxygen. What is the atomic weight of cadmium?

2. The specific heat of cobalt (Co) is 0.10 cal/g. The oxide of cobalt is 78.65 per cent Co. What is the accurate atomic weight of this metal?

3. The specific heat of aluminum is 0.22 cal/g. 3.00 g. of aluminum form 5.67 g. of aluminum oxide. Calculate the accurate atomic weight of aluminum.

4. A 3.04-g. sample of magnesium displaces from hydrochloric acid 0.254 g. of hydrogen. The specific heat of magnesium is 0.25 cal/g. Calculate the atomic weight of this metal.

5. An oxide of uranium (U) contains 10.000 g. of uranium to 2.0150 g. of oxygen. The specific heat of uranium is 0.0256 cal/g. Find the equivalent weight and the atomic weight. What is the formula of the oxide?

6. How many atoms of carbon are in one molecule of: (a) benzene, (b) methyl alcohol, and (c) ethyl ether? (See table on page 43.)

7. Silicon forms a number of volatile compounds. Molecular-weight determinations and analysis of several of these compounds gave the results shown in the table below.

COMPOUND	MOL. WT.	% SI	WT. OF SI/MOLE
Silicon tetrachloride, $SiCl_4$	169.89	16.51	
Silicon trichloride, Si_2Cl_6	268.86	20.87	
Chloro silicane, SiH_3Cl	66.54	42.17	
Silicane, SiH_4	32.09	87.44	
Disilicane, Si_2H_6	62.17	90.27	
Trisilicane, Si_3H_8	92.24	91.26	
Tetrasilicane, Si_4H_{10}	122.32	91.76	

(a) What is the approximate atomic weight of silicon? (b) Assuming the analysis of silicon tetrachloride to be correct, find the accurate atomic weight of silicon.

CHAPTER VIII

EXPONENTIAL NUMBERS, LOGARITHMS, AND THE SLIDE RULE

There is a certain amount of satisfaction to be gained from attacking a problem and working it through to the correct numerical answer. Many students are discouraged from gaining this satisfaction by the laborious numerical work involved. It is the purpose of this chapter to discuss means of shortening the time required for this numerical work.

EXPONENTIAL NUMBERS

A little later you will be solving such an expression as $\dfrac{(0.013)^2}{0.10}$. Most students see quickly that the result will contain the sequence of digits 169, since $13 \times 13 = 169$, but they are hesitant about locating the decimal point. Of course, you can arrive at the correct result by long multiplication and division, but this requires a great deal of time. If the method suggested below is followed, the multiplication and division can be performed quickly and with confidence.

$$0.013 = \frac{0.013 \times 100}{100} = \frac{1.3}{100} = \frac{1.3}{10^2} = 1.3 \times 10^{-2} \text{ *}$$

$$0.10 = \frac{0.10 \times 10}{10} = \frac{1.0}{10} = 1 \times 10^{-1}$$

and

$$\frac{(0.013)^2}{0.10} = \frac{(1.3 \times 10^{-2})^2}{10^{-1}} = \frac{(1.3)^2 \times (10^{-2})^2}{10^{-1}} = \frac{1.69 \times 10^{-4}}{10^{-1}}$$

$$= 1.69 \times 10^{-4} \times 10 = 1.69 \times 10^{-3}$$

* The significance of negative exponents is nothing more or less than is indicated in the last step of this operation.

As another example, simplify

$$\frac{1200 \times 600}{0.07}$$

$$1200 = 120 \times 10 = 12 \times 10^2 = 1.2 \times 10^3$$

$$600 = 60 \times 10 = 6 \times 10^2$$

$$0.07 = \frac{0.7}{10} = \frac{7}{100} = \frac{7}{10^2} = 7 \times 10^{-2}$$

Then,

$$\frac{1200 \times 600}{0.07} = \frac{1.2 \times 10^3 \times 6 \times 10^2}{7 \times 10^{-2}} = \frac{1.2 \times 6}{7} \times 10^3 \times 10^2 \times 10^2$$

$$= \frac{1.2 \times 6}{7} \times 10^7 = \frac{7.2}{7} \times 10^7 = 1.03 \times 10^7$$

These calculations seem rather long, but once you have gained confidence in expressing numbers in terms of powers of 10 you will be able to omit most of the foregoing steps.

Notice above that 1200 has been expressed in three other ways: 120×10, 12×10^2, and 1.2×10^3. It could be expressed as 0.12×10^4, 0.012 and 10^5, etc. *It is conventional in expressing numbers exponentially to leave one digit to the left of the decimal point.* Thus $1200 = 1.2 \times 10^3$. The main reason for choosing this convention is that when it is used the exponent of the ten shows the size of the quantity. For example, if the exponent is 6, the number is in the millions; and if the exponent is -2, the number is in the hundredths.

From the illustrative examples above, you should see that

1. *When an ordinary number is expressed exponentially the power of the 10 is equal to the number of places the decimal point has been moved; this power is positive if the decimal point has been moved to the left and negative if the decimal point has been moved to the right.*

According to this generalization, $1600 = 1.6 \times 10^3$ and $0.0053 = 5.3 \times 10^{-3}$. These results may be checked step by step as follows.

$$1600 = 1600 \times \frac{10^3}{10^3} = \frac{1600}{10^3} \times 10^3 = \frac{1600}{1000} \times 10^3 = 1.6 \times 10^3$$

or

$$1600 = 160 \times 10 = 16 \times 10 \times 10 =$$

$$1.6 \times 10 \times 10 \times 10 = 1.6 \times 10^3$$

and

$$0.0053 = 0.0053 \times \frac{10^3}{10^3} = \frac{0.0053}{10^3} \times 1000 = \frac{5.3}{10^3} = 5.3 \times 10^{-3}$$

or

$$0.0053 = \frac{0.053}{10} = \frac{0.53}{10 \times 10} = \frac{5.3}{10 \times 10 \times 10} = \frac{5.3}{10^3} = 5.3 \times 10^{-3}$$

2. In multiplying powers of 10, the exponents are added, i.e., $10^a \times 10^b = 10^{a+b}$. For example, $10^2 \times 10^3 = 10^5$, because $10^2 = 100$, $10^3 = 1000$, and $10^2 \times 10^3 = 100 \times 1000 = 100,000 = 10^5$.

3. In dividing powers of 10, the exponent of the denominator is subtracted from that of the numerator, i.e., $\frac{10^c}{10^b} = 10^{c-b}$. For example, $\frac{10^5}{10^3} = 10^{5-3} = 10^2$, because $10^5 = 100,000$, $10^3 = 1000$, and $\frac{10^5}{10^3} = \frac{100,000}{1000} = 100 = 10^2$.

Problems

1. Show that $16,000 = 1.6 \times 10^4$, $0.00271 = 2.71 \times 10^{-3}$, and $0.05 = 5 \times 10^{-2}$.

2. Express exponentially in the conventional way: (a) 8000, (b) 0.7, (c) 950,000,000, and (d) 0.000,00015.   *Ans.* (a) 8×10^3.

3. Express as ordinary numbers (a) 3.51×10^6, (b) 1.6×10^{-5}, and (c) 6.023×10^{23}.

4. Simplify exponentially: (a) 0.071×160, (b) $\frac{1800 \times 22}{0.07}$, (c) 15,000,-000 $\times$ 150, and (d) $\frac{400 \times 800 \times 270}{700 \times 300}$.

5. The weight of an atom of oxygen is $\frac{16.00}{6.023 \times 10^{23}}$ g. Express this as a decimal fraction and as an exponential number.

LOGARITHMS

The logarithm (often abbreviated log) of a number is the power to which 10 must be raised to yield the given number.* Thus, since

$$1{,}000{,}000 = 10^6 \quad \text{and} \quad 10{,}000 = 10^4$$

$$\log 1{,}000{,}000 = 6 \qquad \log 10{,}000 = 4$$

Further,

$$1{,}000{,}000 \times 10{,}000 = 10^6 \times 10^4 = 10^{10}$$

$$\log (1{,}000{,}000 \times 10{,}000) = \log (10^6 \times 10^4) = \log 10^{10} = 10$$

Notice that the log of a product of two numbers equals the sum of the logs of the numbers, or

$$\log (M \times N) = \log M + \log N \;†$$

Similarly, since

$$\frac{1{,}000{,}000}{10{,}000} = \frac{10^6}{10^4} = 10^6 \times 10^{-4} = 10^2 = 100$$

$$\log \frac{1{,}000{,}000}{10{,}000} = \log (10^6 \times 10^{-4}) = 6 + (-4) = 2 = \log 100$$

This is an example of the general rule that

log of a quotient = log of the numerator − log of the denominator

In all the examples above only whole number powers of 10 are used, i.e., all the logs are whole numbers. But the same principles apply when the exponents (logs) are not integers.

---

* This type of logarithm is called the *common* log in order to distinguish it from another type called the natural logarithm which is abbreviated $\log_e$ or ln. The relation between the two logarithms is

$$2.303 \log N = \ln N$$

We shall use only common logs in our discussion here.

† Of course, this applies similarly to three or more numbers.

It is obvious that from the definition of logarithms,

$\log 1 = \log 10^0 = 0$

log of any number between 1 and

$\log 10 = \log 10^1 = 1$ 10 is between 0 and 1.

log of any number between 10 and

$\log 100 = \log 10^2 = 2$ 100 is between 1 and 2.

log of any number between 100 and

$\log 1000 = \log 10^3 = 3$ 1000 is between 2 and 3.

log of any number between 1000 and

$\log 10,000 = \log 10^4 = 4$ 10,000 is between 3 and 4.

For example,

$$\log 5.6 = 0.7482$$

$$\log 56 = 1.7482$$

$$\log 560 = 2.7482$$

$$\log 5600 = 3.7482$$

Notice that logs are divided into two parts. The part to the right of the decimal point is called the *mantissa* and that to the left of the decimal point is called the *characteristic*. Notice further that the mantissa is determined by the sequence of the digits and is independent of the location of the decimal. The size of the characteristic, on the other hand, depends entirely on the position of the decimal point. In fact, it is seen from the examples above that in dealing with *numbers greater than 1, the characteristic of the log is 1 less than the number of digits to the left of the decimal point.*

Concerning numbers less than 1, consider this:

$$\log 0.56 = \log \frac{5.6}{10} = \log 5.6 - \log 10 = 0.7482 - 1$$

However, it is conventional to write this in another form, thus:

$$\log 0.56 = 0.7482 - 1 = -1 + 0.7482 = \bar{1}.7482 \text{ *}$$

* Sometimes another convention is used, and this log is written $9.7482 - 10$.

The negative sign over the characteristic indicates that the characteristic is negative, but the mantissa is still positive. Similarly,

$$\log 0.056 = \bar{2}.7482$$

$$\log 0.0056 = \bar{3}.7482$$

From these examples we see that *for numbers less than 1, the characteristic of the log is negative and is numerically 1 more than the number of zeros between the decimal and the first other digit to the right.*

The characteristic of the log of any number can be found by use of the two rules above, but the mantissas which are not integers but fractions must be found in tables. Such a table is given inside the back cover.

The Use of Logarithms. First you should become familiar with the use of the log table. To do this you should not only be able to find the log of any given number but should also be able to find the number corresponding to a given log. Such a number is called the *antilog*.

Illustrative Example

1. What is the log of 95?
Solution. Since there are two digits to the left of the decimal, the characteristic is 1, and according to the table the mantissa is .9777; therefore, the log is 1.9777.

2. What is the log of 7.03?
Solution. The characteristic is 0, and the mantissa is .8470. The log is therefore 0.8470.

3. What is the log of 0.0564?
Solution. The characteristic is $\bar{2}$, and the mantissa is .7513. The log is then $\bar{2}.7513$.

4. What is the log of 8044?
Solution. The characteristic is 3. To find the mantissa in the table, interpolation is necessary, since numbers beyond three digits are not listed in this table. The mantissa of 8040 is .9053, and that of 8050 is .9058. The difference between these is .0005, and $\frac{4}{10}$ of this difference

is .0002. Therefore, the mantissa of 8044 is .9053 + 0.0002 = .9055, and the log of 8044 is 3.9055.*

5. What is the antilog of 1.7459?

Solution. In the table we find that the mantissa .7459 corresponds to the sequence of digits 557. Since the characteristic is 1, there are two digits to the left of the decimal; the antilog is 55.7.

Problems

1. Find the logs of (a) 26, (b) 4.05, (c) 0.0065, and (d) 9755.

2. What numbers have the following logs: (a) 1.8451, (b) 0.1790, (c) $\bar{3}.1931$, (d) 2.8460, and (e) 6.8690?

Illustrative Problems

Multiplication and Division by Means of Logs

1. Using logs, solve 68.7 × 13.9.

Solution. Since the log of a product of numbers equals the sum of the logs of the individual numbers,

log (68.7 × 13.9) = log 68.7 + log 13.9 = 1.8370 + 1.1430 = 2.9800
Antilog of 2.9800 = 955 †

2. Solve $\dfrac{74.4}{65.0}$

Solution. Since the log of a quotient equals the log of the numerator minus the log of the denominator,

$$\log \frac{74.4}{65.0} = \log 74.4 - \log 65 = 1.8716 - 1.8129 = 0.0587$$

The antilog of this is 1.144.

3. In a typical gas law problem the final numerical work reduces to an operation of the type

$$\text{Volume} = 120 \times \frac{740}{760} \times \frac{273}{298} \text{ cc.}$$

Solve this by means of logs.

---

* This interpolation can also be accomplished by use of the proportional parts table on the right of the table of logarithms.

† By long multiplication 68.7 × 13.9 = 954.93 instead of 955. Before deciding that logs are not accurate, consider the following chapter on "Significant Figures."

Solution.

$$\log \text{ of} \left(120 \times \frac{740}{760} \times \frac{273}{298}\right) = \log (120 \times 740 \times 273)$$
$$- \log (760 \times 298)$$

$$= (\log 120 + \log 740 + \log 273)$$
$$- (\log 760 + \log 298)$$

$$= (2.0792 + 2.8692 + 2.4362)$$
$$- (2.8808 + 2.4742)$$

$$= 2.0296$$

The antilog of 2.0296 is 107. Therefore,

$$\text{Volume} = 120 \times \frac{740}{760} \times \frac{273}{298} = 107 \text{ cc.}$$

4. Solve $\dfrac{18.1 \times 5.66}{0.94 \times 0.087}$.

Solution.

$$\log \frac{18.1 \times 5.66}{0.94 \times 0.087} = \log (18.1 \times 5.66) - \log (0.94 \times 0.087)$$

$$= \log 18.1 + \log 5.66 - (\log 0.94 + \log 0.087)$$

$$= 1.2577 + 0.7528 - (\bar{1}.9731 + \bar{2}.9395)$$

$$= 2.0105 - \bar{2}.9126$$

This subtraction requires some thought, since part of the number being subtracted ($\bar{2}.9126$) is negative, whereas part of it is positive. This operation can be performed in either of two ways. The most obvious method, perhaps, is to convert this composite number $\bar{2}.9126$ into a totally negative number. It is $-2 + 0.9126 = -1.0874$. Then

$$2.0105 - \bar{2}.9126 = 2.0105 - (-1.0874) = 2.0105 + 1.0874$$

$$= 3.0979$$

The antilog of 3.0979 = 1253.

The subtraction above ($2.0105 - \bar{2}.9126$) can be performed more rapidly but with more chance of error by adding the characteristic, since $-(-2) = +2$, and subtracting the mantissa. Thus,

$$2.0105 - \bar{2}.9126 = 4.0105 - 0.9126 = 3.0979$$

Problems

1. Solve the following by use of logarithms.

(a) $70 \times \dfrac{700}{760} \times \dfrac{273}{300}$.

(b) $16 \times 10 \times 4.1$.

(c) $\dfrac{900}{22.5}$.

(d) $\dfrac{25 \times 14}{0.65}$.

$\qquad$ *Ans.* (a) = 58.7; (b) = 656; (c) = 40.0; (d) = 53.83.

2. Find by use of logs the weight of 22.4 l. of oxygen whose density is 1.43 g/l.

3. What volume will 50.0 cc. of a gas at 700 mm. and 27° C. occupy under standard conditions? *Ans.* 41.9 cc.

4. The density of mercury is 13.55 g/cc. What is the weight of 8.70 cc. of this metal? *Ans.* 118 g.

5. What volume is occupied by 35.5 g. of silver whose density is 10.5 g/cc.? *Ans.* 3.38 cc.

Powers and Roots. Logs are especially useful in raising to powers and extracting roots. Since $8^3 = 8 \times 8 \times 8$, it follows that $\log 8^3 = \log (8 \times 8 \times 8) = \log 8 + \log 8 + \log 8 = 3 \log 8 = 3 \times 0.9031 = 2.7093$, whose antilog is 512. In general, $\log N^a = a \log N$.

Since a root can be written as a power, the extraction of a root is essentially the same as raising to a power. For example,

$$\sqrt{8} = 8^{\frac{1}{2}}$$

$$\log \sqrt{8} = \log 8^{\frac{1}{2}} = \tfrac{1}{2} \log 8 = \frac{0.9031}{2} = 0.4516$$

The antilog of 0.4516 is 2.83. Then $\sqrt{8} = 2.83$.

Illustrative Examples

1. What is the cube of 6.1?
Solution.

$$\log (6.1)^3 = 3 \log 6.1 = 3 \times 0.7853 = 2.3559$$

The antilog is 227. Then $(6.1)^3 = 227$.

2. What is the $\sqrt{17}$?

Solution.

$$\log \sqrt{17} = \log 17^{\frac{1}{2}} = \frac{1}{2} \log 17 = \frac{1}{2} \times 1.2304 = 0.6152$$

whose antilog is 4.12.

3. Solve $\dfrac{\sqrt{15} \times 9.1}{(4.2)^2 \times 17}$.

Solution.

$$\log \frac{\sqrt{15} \times 9.1}{(4.2)^2 \times 17} = \log [\sqrt{15} \times 9.1] - \log [(4.2)^2 \times 17]$$

$$= \log \sqrt{15} + \log 9.1 - [\log (4.2)^2 + \log 17]$$

$$= \frac{\log 15}{2} + \log 9.1 - [2 \log 4.2 + \log 17]$$

$$= \frac{1.1761}{2} + 0.9590 - [2(0.6232) + 1.2304]$$

$$= 0.5881 + 0.9590 - [1.2464 + 1.2304]$$

$$= 1.5471 - 2.4768 = -0.9297$$

Now we cannot find a negative mantissa in the table. In order to obtain a positive mantissa we add 1 to the mantissa and subtract 1 from the characteristic, thus,

$$\log \frac{\sqrt{15} \times 9.1}{(4.2)^2 \times 17} = -0.9297 = 1 - 0.9297 - 1 = \overline{1}.0703$$

The antilog is 0.118.

Problems

1. What is the cube root of 17? *   *Ans.* 2.571.

2. What are the squares of the following numbers: (*a*) 18, (*b*) 4.12, (*c*) 0.0085?   *Ans.* (*a*) 324, (*b*) 16.97, (*c*) 0.00007225 or 7.225×10^{-5}.

3. Solve by use of logs: (*a*) $\sqrt{(17)^3}$ and (*b*) $\sqrt{19 \times 5}$.

THE SLIDE RULE

The slide rule is a mechanical device by means of which certain mathematical operations such as multiplication, division, and root extraction can be performed rapidly. The principles involved in the use of the slide rule are the principles of logarithms, and for this reason the rule is considered to be a mechanical log table.

* Try solving this without using logs!

Multiplication and Division. The essential parts of a typical slide rule are shown in Fig. 1. This rule has four scales, A, B, C, and $D;$ but for multiplication and division only the C and D scales are needed. These are logarithmic scales; that is to say, the divisions correspond to the logs of the numbers from 1 to 10, although the numbers and not the logs are engraved on the scales.

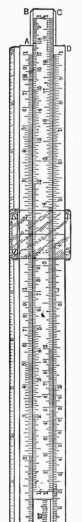

Remember that in multiplying numbers by use of logs, the logs are added. To multiply 2 by 3 using the slide rule, set the 1 on the C scale over the 2 on the D scale and then move the vertical hair line of the runner over 3 on the C scale. The product 6 is found under the hair line on the D scale. These operations really involve adding to the log of 2 the log of 3 and finding the resulting antilog, 6.

Division is just the reverse of multiplication. To divide 6 by 3, set 3 on the C scale above 6 on the D scale, and read off below 1 on the C scale the quotient 2 on the D scale.

At this point you should practice by using the rule for a few simple multiplications (2×2 and 2×4) and divisions ($8 \div 2$ and $8 \div 4$).

Now if you attempt to multiply 2×6 just as you did 2×4 you will find that the product is off the scale. In such cases move the C scale to the left instead of to the right. Set the 1 on the right end of the C scale over the 2 on the D scale and read off below the 6 on the C scale the product 12 on the D scale.

Notice that the rule does not point off decimals. This is not serious; the decimal can usually be located quickly by a rough mental calculation. For example, by use of the slide rule $\dfrac{4.8 \times 9.2}{95 \times 0.21} = 221$. To locate

FIG. 1 *

the decimal, notice that 9.2 goes into 95 about 10 times; therefore, the quotient is approximate

$$\frac{4.8}{10 \times 0.21} = \frac{4.8}{2.1} = 2.3.$$ The correct result is then 2.21.

* Reprinted by permission from Eshbach "Handbook of Engineering Fundamentals," John Wiley and Sons.

Problems

1. Solve by means of (a) long multiplication and division, (b) logs and (c) slide rule

$$116 \times \frac{711}{760} \times \frac{273}{298}$$

Compare the time required in each.

Ans. 99.4, and the times are in order 3, 1.5 and 1 min.

2. Solve with and without the aid of logs

$$\frac{\sqrt{39} \times 17}{(3.9)^2 \times 21}$$ *Ans.* 0.332.

3. The diameter of a hydrogen molecule is 2.47×10^{-8} cm. How many of these molecules would form a line 1 cm. long?

4. The actual average speed in centimeters per second of oxygen molecules at 27° C. is

$$\sqrt{\frac{3 \times 8.315 \times 300 \times 10^7}{32}}$$

(a) Solve this, and (b) express the results in miles per hours.

CHAPTER IX

SIGNIFICANT FIGURES

Suppose you are weighing a piece of zinc using a set of weights whose smallest weight is 0.01 g. When you place 16.51 g. on the right-hand pan, the pointer swings slightly to the right, and when an additional 0.01 g. is added, the pointer swings about an equal distance to the left. How would you record the weight? It is obvious that it is 16.51 plus an additional amount less than 0.01 g. If in recording this weight you should confine yourself to certain figures, you would record 16.51 g. But, if you should do this, you would not be recording the weight as accurately as you know it, for you know that it is very close to halfway between 16.51 and 16.52. *Scientists have agreed that in expressing the results of measurements, besides all the certain figures one uncertain figure should be retained.* According to this convention, you should record the weight of the zinc as 16.515 g. This last 5 is uncertain; it could be 4 or 6.

Suppose further that you should wish to express this weight of zinc in terms of gram-atomic weights. You could by long division find

$$\text{No. of gram-atomic weights of zinc} = \frac{16.515}{65.38} = 0.2526002$$

Now the question as to whether you have taken the answer to a sufficient number of figures should arise in your mind. Should you continue the division or have you already taken the answer beyond the point justified by the data? To decide this, we need only recall that the weight of the zinc lies between 16.514 and 16.516 and similarly that the atomic weight lies between 65.37 and 65.39.

Using the lower limit of the weight and the upper limit of the atomic weight, we obtain as the number of gram-atomic weights of zinc

$$\frac{16.514}{65.39} = 0.252546$$

On the other hand, if we use the upper limit of the weight with the lower limit of the atomic weight, we obtain

$$\frac{16.516}{65.37} = 0.252\underline{654}$$

Notice that these three possible answers are the same to only three figures. However, the first answer is far more probable than either of the two extreme values. Therefore, we express the answer to four significant figures as 0.2526.

Consider now this problem involving a simple multiplication: What weight of oxygen, whose density is 1.4290 g/l., is required to fill a 6.55-liter vessel?

By long multiplication, weight of oxygen = $1.4290 \times 6.55 = 9.359950$ g. Are we justified in retaining seven figures? The density lies between 1.4289 and 1.4291, and the volume between 6.54 and 6.56. The extreme values for the weight are then

$$1.4289 \times 6.54 = 9.345\underline{006} \text{ g.}$$

$$1.4291 \times 6.56 = 9.374\underline{896} \text{ g.}$$

These three possible answers agree to only two figures; however, since the first answer is much more probable than either of the extreme values, we give the answer to three figures as 9.36 grams.*

These two problems have been discussed to illustrate the following simple rule: *In multiplication and division, the number of significant figures in the result is equal to the smallest number of significant figures in any item of the data.†*

In regard to significant figures in addition and subtraction, consider this problem: Three students withdrew separately from the same buret 10 cc., 10.1 cc., and 10.12 cc. of solution.‡ What total volume was withdrawn?

Using the given figures, we obtain for the total volume 30.22 cc. However, assuming the data were recorded according to the convention, the lower limits might have been 9, 10.0, and 10.11 cc. respectively, and the sum of these is only 29.11; whereas the upper limits might have been 11, 10.2, and 10.13, and the sum of

* In rejecting superfluous figures, increase by 1 the last figure retained if the following rejected figure is 5 or more.

† In this statement we sacrifice strict accuracy for the sake of practical simplicity. The rule as stated is good enough for ordinary calculations.

‡ Obviously these students were not concerned with the same degree of accuracy.

these is 31.33 cc. These three possible results agree to only one figure, but since the first is much more probable, we express the sum to two significant figures as 30 cc. This illustrates the general rule: *The result in an addition or subtraction should be extended only so far as the position in which the first uncertainty appears in any of the data.* Thus, in the example above, the position in which the first uncertainty appears is the unit position in the first volume, 10 cc., and therefore, the resulting sum will be uncertain in the unit position. It should be expressed only to a whole number of cubic centimeters.

Notice that the general rule that applies to multiplication and division does not necessarily apply to addition and subtraction. For example, the sum of $4.1 + 3.2 + 0.01$ is 7.3 and not just 7. The number of significant figures in a sum or difference can be more than the number of significant figures in the item of data with the smallest number of significant figures.

In a long calculation involving a large number of separate steps, much work and worry can be saved by rounding off the result of each step to the correct number of significant figures before proceeding with the next step. Furthermore, even in simple calculations much time and work can be wisely saved by discarding useless figures before beginning the calculation. Thus

$$1.193 \times 79.35 \times 1.10 = 104.131005$$

by long multiplication. To the correct number of significant figures this rounds off to 104. The same result can be obtained much more easily by first reducing each item of the data to three figures. When this is done we obtain

$$1.19 \times 79.4 \times 1.10 = 103.9 \text{ or } 104$$

This time-saving device of discarding unnecessary figures can be very profitably applied to the use of atomic weights. In the table at the front of this manual you will find the accurate atomic weights in so far as they are known. In some cases these are expressed to six significant figures; but *in many of your calculations rounded off values of atomic weights are sufficient.* For example, suppose you wished to find the number of gram-atomic weights of silver in 100 grams of silver.

$$\text{Number of gram-atomic weights of Ag} = \frac{100}{\text{Atomic weight of Ag}}$$

Would you use the value 107.880 for the atomic weight of silver? Of course not. Since the answer would contain only three significant figures, you would use 108. Then,

$$\text{Number of gram-atomic weights of Ag} = \frac{100}{108} = 0.926$$

Naturally, the accurate value of the atomic weight could be used. But much more work would be required to arrive at essentially the same result. (Show this.)

Some of you may feel that all this simplification is contrary to what you have learned in mathematics, in which you were taught, for example, that

$$10 + 10.1 + 10.12 = 30.22$$

Yet we have just tried to lead you to the conclusion that in finding the total of three separate volumes

$$10 \text{ cc.} + 10.1 \text{ cc.} + 10.12 \text{ cc.} = 30 \text{ cc.}$$

Does this prove that the chemist is simply careless or lazy? No! The apparent discrepancy lies in the fact that the mathematician is dealing with pure numbers. By 10 he really means $10.00000\cdots$, and by 30.22 he means $30.2200000\cdots$. The mathematician simply does not express, in fact, cannot express, all the zeros. When a chemist, however, says he has withdrawn a certain number of cubic centimeters from a buret, *he is trying to represent a physical quantity by a number, and he can only approximate the extent of this quantity in terms of numbers.* If a chemist "withdraws 10.12 cc. from a buret," he merely is withdrawing somewhere between 10.11 and 10.13 cc.* It would be a pure accident if he withdrew $10.1200000\cdots$cc. in a mathematical sense even though he tried thousands of times. Unlike the mathematician, the chemist does not drop zeros when they are significant. (The mathematician is forced to drop them, since there is an infinite number.) Therefore, if a chemist records a volume as 10.00 cc., he means that he measured the volume to the nearest 0.01 cc.

---

* You may, perhaps, wonder why the chemist never expresses volumes withdrawn from a buret to thousandths of a cubic centimeter. Why does he not express the volume as 10.120 cc.? The answer is: He cannot read the buret to thousandths of a cubic centimeter. An ordinary buret is calibrated in tenths. It can be read directly in tenths, but the hundredths must be estimated.

and found it to be 10.00 cc. Thus, you see that 10.00 cc. and 10 cc. are quite different.

There is one other minor point that should be made clear. It concerns locating the decimal point. If there are more digits to the left of the decimal point than there are significant figures, small figures should be used in the uncertain positions, or else the results should be expressed exponentially. For instance, if we know a certain quantity of heat to be thirty thousand five hundred and fifty calories to four significant figures we would express this as

$$30,550 \text{ cal. or } 3.055 \times 10^4 \text{ cal.}$$

From this we see that zeros which are used simply to locate the decimal point are not significant figures. The location of the decimal point depends on the size of the unit in terms of which the quantity is expressed. For example,

25.5 g. (3 significant figures) = 0.0255 kg. (3 significant figures)

Now we are in a position to answer a question which very likely came into your mind at the beginning of this discussion: Why worry about significant figures anyway?

The reasons are these.

1. By carrying only the necessary number of figures you save yourself much work and decrease the chance of errors.

2. To express a result to a greater number of figures than is significant is misleading (scientifically, this is the real reason).

Henceforth you will be expected to express the answers to all problems to the correct number of significant figures. A four-place log table gives results to four significant figures, and an ordinary 10-in. slide rule to three significant figures.

Illustrative Problems

1. 1.5 is what per cent of 17.23?

Solution. Since the answer is to be expressed to only two significant figures, it can be most easily obtained by dividing 1.5 by 17. The result is 8.8%

2. Solve: $(8.276 \times 0.0023) + (0.002036 \times 0.0012)$.

Solution. Each of these two products should be expressed to only two figures; therefore, the same result can be obtained from

$$(8.3 \times 0.0023) + (0.0020 \times 0.0012) = 0.019 + 0.000024 = 0.019$$

Since the second product is smaller than the uncertainty in the first product, it has no effect on the final result.

If this seems surprising to you, consider this. Suppose you are selling lime. The first customer buys 100 lb., the second 75 lb., and the third 125 lb. Now you discover that your scales are sensitive to only + or − a half pound; i.e., they may be in error as much as a half pound. The fourth customer is a lady who wants one-tenth of a pound of lime for her flowers. This you weigh on smaller, more sensitive scales. The question is: How much lime have you sold? (Not how much have you been paid for!) Since the uncertainty in the sum of your first three weights (300 lb.) is possibly as much as 1.5 lb., there is obviously no point in including the one-tenth of a pound in the total.

Problems

1. How many significant figures are there in the number 2.7×10^2, 0.0523, and 2.0? *Ans.* 2, 3 and 2.

2. 0.0811 is what per cent of 1.523? *Ans.* 5.33.

3. One kilogram is 2.2046 lb. How many pounds are there in 50 g.? *Ans.* 0.11.

4. What is the sum of 18.0, 1.53, and 0.09? *Ans.* 19.6.

5. 0.500 is what per cent of 17.53? *Ans.* 2.85.

6. Solve the following.

(a) (2.552×0.0024) g. $+ (1.7 \times 10^{-4})$ g. $- (0.00524 \times 0.061)$ g.

(b) $\dfrac{X^2 \text{ cc.}^2}{0.1 \text{ cc.} - X \text{ cc.}} = 3 \times 10^{-7}$ cc.

7. What would an error of 0.5 g. amount to in terms of per cent in weighing out 500 g.? In 5 g.?

8. What difference is implied between the two numbers, 4.0 and 4.000, when you are referring to experimental data?

9. What is the weight of 2.5 moles of hydrogen?

10. What is the percentage of calcium in calcium sulfate?

11. At zero degrees, 1.85 g. of calcium hydroxide dissolves in a liter of water. Express this solubility in moles per liter.

12. Suppose you buy 2 lb. of sugar at 5 cents per pound. Do you suppose you obtain exactly 2 lb.? If not, would you object to paying 10 cents? Discuss briefly.

13. A 10.0 per cent solution of barium chloride has a density of 1.092 g/cc. What weight of barium chloride is contained in 800 cc. of this solution?

14. Express exponentially 1.0 g. in terms of tons.

15. A length measured with a meter stick calibrated in millimeters is recorded by different observers as 25.2 cm., 25.25 cm., and 25.250 cm. Discuss each of these critically from the standpoint of the conventional method of expressing data.

16. (a) What is the quotient $\frac{9}{7}$, where 9 and 7 are pure numbers? (b) What is the quotient $\frac{9.0}{7.0}$, where 9.0 and 7.0 represent experimental measurements?

CHAPTER X

RELATIVE DENSITY, SPECIFIC GRAVITY

As the name implies, the relative density of a substance is its density relative to the density of some other substance taken as a standard. Unless otherwise stated, the densities to be compared are at the same temperature and pressure. Thus, since the density of oxygen (S.T.P.) is $\dfrac{32}{22.4}$ g/l. and that of hydrogen is $\dfrac{2.0}{22.4}$ g/l., the density of oxygen relative to hydrogen is $\dfrac{32}{22.4} \div \dfrac{2.0}{22.4}$ $= \dfrac{32}{2} = 16$. Similarly, we can calculate the density of oxygen relative to air. It is $\dfrac{32}{29}$, since 22.4 liters of air at S.T.P. weighs 29 grams. In general, the relative density of a gas is equal to the molecular weight of the gas divided by the molecular weight of the other gas (usually hydrogen) being used as the standard. Thus, relative density,

$$D_r = \frac{\text{Molecular weight of the gas}}{\text{Molecular weight of hydrogen}} \tag{1}$$

If the relative density of a gas is known, its molecular weight can be calculated, for, from (1)

Molecular weight of the gas $= D_r \times$ Molecular weight of hydrogen

Notice especially two things in regard to relative densities of gases.
1. Relative densities have no units. (Why?)
2. Relative densities are the same at all temperatures. (Why?)

The relative density of a liquid or solid is given a special name, specific gravity; and water, not hydrogen, is used as the standard.

$$\text{Specific gravity} = \frac{\text{Density of the substance}}{\text{Density of water}}$$

$$= \frac{\text{Weight of some volume of the substance}}{\text{Weight of an equal volume of water}}$$

If the temperature is 4° C., the specific gravity is the same as the density in grams per cubic centimeter except that the specific gravity has no units.

Unlike the relative densities of gases, specific gravities may, and very likely will, vary with temperature. (Why?)

Density is usually more useful than specific gravity because the weight of a given volume can be calculated directly from the density, whereas, in order to calculate the weight of a given volume of a substance from its specific gravity, we must also know the density of water at the given temperature.

$$\text{Weight} = \text{Volume} \times \text{Density}$$

$$= \text{Volume} \times \text{Specific Gravity} \times \text{Density of water}$$

Illustrative Problems

1. If 1000 cc. (S.T.P.) of nitrogen gas weighs 1.2507 g., calculate (a) the density relative to hydrogen, and (b) the molecular weight of nitrogen.

Solution. Using hydrogen as the standard,

$$D_r = \frac{\text{Density of N}_2}{\text{Density of H}_2} = \frac{1.2507 \text{ g/l.}}{0.08987 \text{ g/l.}} = 13.92$$

Molecular weight of nitrogen = $D_r \times$ Molecular weight of hydrogen

$$= 13.92 \times 2.016 = 28.06$$

2. A bottle weighs 10.10 g. When filled with water at 4° C., it weighs 51.72 g., and when filled with a certain oil, it weighs 44.04 g. Calculate (a) the capacity of the bottle; (b) the specific gravity of the oil.

Solution.

$$\text{Weight of water} = 51.72 - 10.10 = 41.62 \text{ g.}$$

$$\text{Weight of oil} = 44.04 - 10.10 = 33.94 \text{ g.}$$

(a) The density of water at 4° C. is 1.000 g/cc.; therefore,

$$\text{Capacity of the bottle} = 41.62 \text{ cc.} \quad Ans.$$

(b)

$$\text{Specific gravity of the oil} = \frac{\text{Weight of the oil}}{\text{Weight of the water}} = \frac{33.94}{41.62} = 0.8154.$$
$$Ans.$$

3. A 100-cc. volumetric flask which has not been calibrated requires 99.20 g. of water at 25° C. to fill it. At the same temperature, 168.5 g. of sulfuric acid fills the flask. The absolute density of water at 25° is 0.9970 g/cc. Calculate (a) the specific gravity of the acid, (b) the true volume of the flask, and (c) the density of the acid.

Solution.

(a) Specific gravity $= \dfrac{168.5}{99.20} = 1.699 \quad Ans.$

(b) $V = \dfrac{\text{Weight of water}}{\text{Density of water}} = \dfrac{99.20}{0.9970} = 99.50 \text{ cc.} \quad Ans.$

(c) Density of the acid = Specific gravity × density of water = 1.699 × 0.9970 = 1.694 g/cc.
or

$$\text{Density of the acid} = \frac{\text{Weight}}{\text{Volume}} = \frac{168.5}{99.50} = 1.694 \text{ g/cc.} \quad Ans.$$

Problems

1. (a) The specific gravity of turpentine is 0.8730. One gallon of water weighs 8.345 lb. What is the weight of one gallon of turpentine?
Ans. 7.287 lb.

(b) What volume will 50 lb. of turpentine occupy? *Ans.* 6.9 gal.

2. The specific gravity of gold is 19.3. What weight of gold will displace 4.75 cc. of water at 4°? *Ans.* 91.7 g.

3. Under standard conditions, 100 cc. of a certain gas weighs 0.1964 g. Calculate (a) the relative density of the gas compared with hydrogen and (b) the molecular weight of the gas.

4. Calculate the absolute densities at S.T.P. and the relative densities of hydrogen chloride, chlorine, and ammonia. (See atomic weight table.)

5. The relative densities of hydrogen sulfide, carbon dioxide, and nitrogen are 17, 22, and 14 respectively. Calculate the densities of these gases under S.T.P.

6. If 100 cc. of a certain liquid at 4° C. weighs 125 g., what is its (a) specific gravity and (b) its density?

7. Sulfuric acid, containing 92.10 per cent H_2SO_4, has a specific gravity of 1.83.* What volume of this acid contains 10 g. of H_2SO_4?

8. A piece of metal weighs 5.90 g. in air and 5.30 g. when immersed in water at 4° C. Calculate (a) the specific gravity of the metal and (b) the volume of 100 grams of the metal.

9. The specific gravity of iron is 7.28 at 25° C. Calculate the weight of a cube of iron 4.0 cm. on edge. The density of water at 25° C. is 0.997 g/cc.

10. At 20° C. nitric acid, which is 70.0 per cent HNO_3, has a specific gravity of 1.421. The density of water at 20° C. is 0.998 g/cc. Calculate the volume of this acid which contains 25.0 g. of HNO_3.

* When no temperature is stated, you may assume that it is 4° C.

CHAPTER XI

THE USE OF CHEMICAL UNITS OF QUANTITY

You have already learned the meaning of the terms gram-atomic weight, gram-molecular weight (mole), and gram-equivalent weight. These are chemical units of quantity. In this chapter we shall show the use of these in the solution of chemical problems.

PROBLEMS BASED ON CHEMICAL EQUATIONS

Problems of this type have already been discussed in Chapter V. There you worked in terms of physical units (grams, pounds, etc.). Now these problems will be discussed in terms of chemical units. The reasons for doing this are:

1. In order to solve certain future problems, those in the next section on "Solutions," for example, it is necessary that you think in terms of chemical units.

2. This method of attack usually shortens your work. This will become increasingly true as the problems become longer and more complex.

You learned in Chapter V how to interpret chemical equations. You know, for example, that the equation

$$2KClO_3 = 2KCl + 3O_2$$

tells us that 2 gram-molecular weights (moles) of potassium chlorate yield 2 gram-molecular weights (moles) of potassium chloride and 3 gram-molecular weights (moles) of oxygen. Notice that the number of moles of potassium chloride obtained is equal to the number of moles of potassium chlorate decomposed, whereas the number of moles of oxygen is $\frac{3}{2}$ times the number of moles of potassium chlorate decomposed. From this information and knowledge of the molecular weights of these compounds it is a simple matter to calculate the number of moles or the number of grams of either potassium chloride or oxygen that can be obtained from a given number of moles or grams of potassium chlorate. Consider the following illustrative problems and notice that *the only new idea here is that of thinking in terms of chemical units.*

Illustrative Problems

1. (*a*) How many moles of oxygen can be obtained by heating 7.00 moles of potassium chlorate?

Solution. The equation of the reaction is: $2KClO_3 = 2KCl + 3O_2$. This equation tells us that the number of moles of oxygen obtained is $\frac{3}{2}$ times the number of moles of potassium chlorate heated. Therefore, seven moles of the chlorate will yield $\frac{3}{2} \times 7.00 = 10.5$ moles of oxygen.

Ans.

(*b*) What weight of oxygen in grams can be obtained from 7.00 moles of potassium chlorate?

Solution. In part (*a*) we found that 7.00 moles of the chlorate yield 10.5 moles of oxygen. Since 1 mole of oxygen is 32.0 g., the weight of the oxygen will be $10.5 \times 32.0 = 336$ g. *Ans.*

(*c*) How many moles of the chlorate need be heated in order to obtain 50.0 g. of oxygen?

Solution. 1 mole of oxygen requires $\frac{2}{3}$ mole $KClO_3$. (See equation.)

$$50.0 \text{ g. of oxygen} = \frac{50.0}{32.0} \text{ moles of oxygen, since 1 mole of oxygen} = 32.0 \text{ g.}$$

Then, $\dfrac{50.0}{32.0}$ moles of oxygen require

$$\frac{2}{3} \times \frac{50.0}{32.0} = \frac{100}{96.0} = 1.04 \text{ moles } KClO_3. \quad Ans.$$

(*d*) What weight of oxygen can be obtained by heating 60.0 g. of $KClO_3$?

Solution. According to the equation,

$$2KClO_3 = 2KCl + 3O_2$$

the number of moles of oxygen produced $= \frac{3}{2} \times$ number of moles of $KClO_3$ used.

$$\text{Number of moles of } KClO_3 \text{ used} = \frac{\text{Weight of } KClO_3}{\text{Molecular weight } KClO_3}$$

$$= \frac{60.0}{122.6} \text{ moles}$$

$$\text{Number of moles of } O_2 = \frac{3}{2} \times \frac{60.0}{122.6}$$

$$\text{Weight of } O_2 = \text{Number of moles} \times \text{Weight of 1 mole}$$

$$= \frac{3}{2} \times \frac{60.0}{122.6} \times 32 \text{ g.} = 23.5 \text{ g.} \quad Ans.$$

When the answer to a problem has been obtained, it is always advisable to glance back over the problem to see if the answer is possibly correct, especially in regard to the decimal point. Here, for example, by returning to the problem we see that we began with a little less than one-half of a mole of $KClO_3$ and would, therefore, obtain slightly less than $\frac{3}{2} \times \frac{1}{2} = \frac{3}{4}$ mole of oxygen. And this will weigh about $\frac{3}{4} \times 32 = 24$ g. Then our answer appears to be correct.

2. Hydrogen sulfate can be prepared from sulfur in three steps as represented by the following equations.

$$S + O_2 = SO_2$$

$$2SO_2 + O_2 = 2SO_3$$

$$SO_3 + H_2O = H_2SO_4$$

(*a*) How many moles of hydrogen sulfate can be obtained from 5 gram-atomic weights of sulfur?

Solution. Referring to the equations, we see that 1 mole of hydrogen sulfate is obtained from 1 gram-atomic weight of sulfur; therefore, 5 moles of hydrogen sulfate will be obtained from 5 gram-atomic weights of sulfur. *Ans.* 5 moles of hydrogen sulfate.

(*b*) What weight of hydrogen sulfate can be obtained from 8.00 g. of sulfur?

Solution. Before solving this problem, we shall introduce a new symbol in order to shorten our work. This new symbol is $\approx$. This symbol is to be read "corresponds to" or "is equivalent to," just as the symbol $=$ reads "is equal to." As an example of the use of this symbol, consider this. Suppose you are selling apples at 20 cents per dozen, and I am selling oranges at 25 cents per dozen, and you wish to exchange some apples for oranges. It follows from these prices that the fair rate of exchange is four dozen oranges for five dozen apples. And we could write

$$4 \text{ dozen oranges} \approx 5 \text{ dozen apples}$$

or

$$1 \text{ dozen oranges} \approx \tfrac{5}{4} \text{ dozen apples} = 15 \text{ apples}$$

Notice that we cannot say

$$4 \text{ dozen oranges} = 5 \text{ dozen apples}$$

Now we are ready to solve problem 2*b*.

$$8.00 \text{ g. of S} = \frac{8.00}{32.1} \text{ g-at. wt. S}$$

since 1 gram-atomic weight is 32.1 g. By referring to the equations for the reactions, we see that 1 gram-atomic weight of sulfur yields 1 mole of hydrogen sulfate; therefore,

$$\frac{8.00}{32.1} \text{ g-at. wt. S} \eqsim \frac{8.00}{32.1} \text{ mole of } H_2SO_4$$

Now if the number of moles of H_2SO_4 is multiplied by the weight of 1 mole of H_2SO_4, we obtain the weight of the H_2SO_4, i.e.,

$$\text{Weight of } H_2SO_4 = \frac{8.00}{32.1} \times 98.1 \text{ g.} = 24.4 \text{ g.} \textit{Ans.}$$

After you have learned thoroughly how to work such problems, your work may be further shortened to simply this.

$$8.00 \text{ g. S} = \frac{8.00}{32.1} \text{ g-at. wt. S} \eqsim \frac{8.00}{32.1} \text{ g-mol. wt. (moles) of } H_2SO_4$$

$$= \frac{8.00}{32.1} \times 98.1 \text{ g. } H_2SO_4 = 24.4 \text{ g. } H_2SO_4. \textit{Ans.}$$

If you find these problems difficult and unfamiliar, the difficulty is not in the principle or reasoning process but merely in the unfamiliar symbols, formulas, and equations. The principle involved is a simple everyday one which you have often used. As an illustration, consider this comparison.

Familiar Problem. Seventeen dollars will yield in exchange how many dimes?

Solution. There are, no doubt, a number of intelligent foreigners who are unable to solve this problem not because they lack reasoning ability but simply because they lack the knowledge of the fact that 1 dollar equals 10 dimes. If this is known it follows directly that, in general,

Number of dimes in a given amt. of money = 10 × Number of dollars

Therefore, in this case,

Number of dimes = 10 × 17 = 170   *Ans.*

Chemical Problem. Ten moles of HgO when heated will yield how many moles of O_2?

Solution. There are, no doubt, some of you who are unable to work this problem, not because you lack the reasoning ability but simply because you lack the knowledge of the fact that $2HgO = 2Hg + O_2$; *

---

* In one respect, this chemical problem is easier than the other in that it is not necessary that we remember the balanced equation, as we must remember that 1 dollar = 10 dimes. We need remember only the reactants and products of the reaction; we can figure out the coefficients.

that is, in words, 2 moles of HgO yield 1 mole of O_2. Knowing this, it follows directly that, in general,

Number of moles of O_2 obtained $= \frac{1}{2} \times$ Number of moles of HgO heated

Therefore, in this case,

Number of moles of $O_2 = \frac{1}{2} \times 10 = 5.0$ moles.   *Ans.*

Problems

1. Carbon dioxide has a molecular weight of 44. What is its gram-molecular weight?

2. Using the table of atomic weights, compute, to four figures, the gram-molecular weight of: HgO, Na_2SO_4, and $C_{12}H_{22}O_{11}$.
                                    Ans. 216.6 g., 142.1 g., and 342.3 g.

3. The molecular weight of acetic acid is 60.05. How many moles are there in 100 g. of this compound?   *Ans.* 1.67.

4. Oxygen can be prepared by heating mercuric oxide, HgO. The equation for the reaction is:

$$2HgO = 2Hg + O_2$$

(*a*) How many moles of oxygen can be obtained from 9.0 moles of HgO?   *Ans.* 4.5.

(*b*) What weight of oxygen can be obtained from 6.0 moles of HgO?
                                                        Ans. 96 g.

(*c*) You need to heat how many moles of HgO in order to obtain 8.0 g. of oxygen?   *Ans.* 0.50 moles.

(*d*) What weight of HgO need be heated in order to obtain 2.0 g. of oxygen?   *Ans.* 27 g.

5. Calcium, when heated in air, combines with oxygen to form the oxide CaO. This oxide reacts with water to form the hydroxide $Ca(OH)_2$. What weight of the hydroxide can be prepared from 5.0 g. of calcium?

Remember that in working problems of this type, the first step is to write balanced equations for the reactions.

6. An excess of chlorine was added to 10.0 g. of iron. The $FeCl_3$ formed was dissolved in water and NaOH added. The resulting $Fe(OH)_3$ was heated until it was all changed into Fe_2O_3. What weight of Fe_2O_3 was obtained?

7. How much phosphoric acid, H_3PO_4, is formed by the action of 80 g. of phosphorus pentoxide on water? The equation for the reaction is:

$$P_2O_5 + 3H_2O = 2H_3PO_4$$

8. What weight of NaOH can be prepared by the action of 92 g. of sodium on water?

9. (a) How many moles and (b) how many grams of oxygen can be obtained by heating 16.9 g. of BaO_2?

10. What weight of water will react with 28 g. of CaO?

Illustrative Problems

Equation Problems Involving Gas Volumes

We learned in Chapter VII that the molar volume of a gas is 22.4 l. at S.T.P., i.e., 1 mole of any gas occupies 22.4 l. at S.T.P. Using this information, we are able to interpret reaction equations involving gases directly in terms of volumes instead of in terms of weights.

1. What volume of hydrogen at S.T.P. can be obtained by treating 10.0 g. of zinc with an excess of H_2SO_4?

$$Zn + H_2SO_4 = ZnSO_4 + H_2$$

Solution. This equation tells us that 1 gram-atomic weight of zinc yields 1 mole H_2. That is, the number of moles of hydrogen obtained equals the number of gram-atomic weights of zinc used.

$$10.0 \text{ g. Zn} = \frac{10.0}{65.4} \text{ g-at. wt. of Zn} \approx \frac{10.0}{65.4} \text{ mole } H_2$$

One mole of hydrogen occupies 22.4 l. at S.T.P.; therefore, the volume occupied by

$$\frac{10.0}{65.4} \text{ moles} = \frac{10.0}{65.4} \times 22.4 = 3.42 \text{ l.} \quad Ans.$$

2. What volume of carbon dioxide measured at 7° C. and 600 mm. can be obtained by the action of hydrochloric acid on 10.0 g. of $CaCO_3$? The equation for the reaction is:

$$CaCO_3 + 2HCl = CaCl_2 + H_3O + CO_2$$

Solution. According to this equation, the number of moles of CO_2 obtained equals the number of moles of $CaCO_3$ used. The molecular weight of $CaCO_3$ is 100; therefore,

$$10.0 \text{ g. CaCO}_3 = \frac{10.0}{100} \text{ moles CaCO}_3 \approx \frac{10.0}{100} \text{ moles CO}_2$$

$$= \frac{10.0}{100} \times 22.4 = 2.24 \text{ l. (S.T.P.)}$$

This volume of gas will occupy V liters at 7° C. and 600 mm. where, by the general gas law,

$$V = 2.24 \times \text{Pressure correction} \times \text{Temperature correction}$$

The pressure decreases from 760 mm. to 600 mm., tending to increase the volume. The temperature increases from 0° to 7° C., tending to increase the volume. Then,

$$V = 2.24 \times \frac{760}{600} \times \frac{280}{273} = 2.91 \text{ l. at 7° C. and 600 mm. } \textit{Ans.}$$

Problems

1. What volume of H_2S at S.T.P. can be obtained by the action of hydrochloric acid on 1 mole of FeS? *Ans.* 22.4 l.

2. Can a larger volume of CO or of CO_2 be obtained by the action of oxygen on a given weight of carbon?

3. What volume of oxygen at S.T.P. can be obtained from 25 g. of $KClO_3$? *Ans.* 6.8 l.

4. It is necessary to heat what weight of HgO to obtain 7.01 l. of O_2 at S.T.P.?

5. What volume of H_2 will be set free by the action of steam on 18 g. of Fe?

6. What weight of calcium is required to set free from water 16.5 l. of hydrogen at S.T.P.?

7. An excess of sulfuric acid is added to 100 g. of zinc. The hydrogen evolved is collected over water at 26° C. and a barometric pressure of 740 mm. Calculate the volume of the "wet" hydrogen.

8. A sample of impure limestone contains 80 per cent $CaCO_3$. What weight of this limestone is required to yield 56 l. of CO_2 at S.T.P.?

CHAPTER XII

THE CONCENTRATION OF SOLUTIONS

MOLAR CONCENTRATIONS

Suppose you dissolve 40 grams of sodium hydroxide in enough water to make a liter of solution, and you wished to record, for future use, the concentration of this solution. You could do this by stating that the solution contains "40 g. of NaOH per liter of solution." This statement is very definite but rather long. You could express the concentration in percentage by weight. If we assume the density of the solution to be 1 g/cc.,

$$\text{Per cent NaOH} = \frac{40}{1000} \times 100 = 4.0$$

Then the concentration of the solution is "4.0% NaOH." This is short but inexact, and in order to get exactness it would be necessary either to weigh the water used or else to determine the density of the solution. Besides, if in the future you wished to use this solution in some chemical reaction, you will find it necessary to change from percentage to some other units of concentration. In short, *physical units of concentration are not directly applicable to chemical problems.* They can be used, but they involve additional calculations which are not necessary when concentrations are expressed in chemical units (moles per liter or gram-equivalent weights per liter). Now let us express the concentration of this solution in terms of the chemical unit, *moles per liter.* Since the molecular weight of NaOH is 40, the solution contains "one mole of NaOH per liter." You may well raise the objection that this is a rather long expression for concentration. It is, and for this reason chemists have agreed to shorten this to "one molar." In general, *the molar concentration of a solution is the number of gram-molecular weights (moles) of solute per liter of solution.* Notice especially that the molar concentration is a number and represents the number of moles of solute per liter of *solution* and not per liter of *water*. Molar concentration is represented by M and is sometimes spoken of as molarity.

To repeat, then, the concentration of the solution above could be expressed as

4.0 per cent NaOH in physical units

and as

1.0 molar NaOH (1.0 M NaOH) in chemical units

Now we wish to show that the concentration in chemical units is by far more useful, since equal volumes of all solution of the same molar concentration contain the same number of molecules. Suppose you wish to use this solution to neutralize hydrochloric acid. Since the molar concentration is known to be one and the equation for the reaction is known to be

$$NaOH + HCl = NaCl + H_2O$$

it should be obvious that the liter of 1 molar NaOH will react with 1 mole of HCl. On the other hand, if it is known only that the solution is 4.0 per cent NaOH (the equation for the reaction being known, of course) a relatively large amount of calculation is necessary in order to calculate the amount of HCl that will react with 1 liter of NaOH solution.*

Illustrative Problems

1. What is the molar concentration of a solution containing 300 g. of H_2SO_4 per liter?

Solution. By definition, the molar concentration (M) is the number of moles of solute per liter of solution. The gram-molecular weight of H_2SO_4 is 98.1 g.; therefore,

$$300 \text{ g. of } H_2SO_4 = \frac{300}{98.1} \text{ moles } H_2SO_4$$

Since this is in 1 liter of solution, the concentration is $\frac{300}{98.1} = 3.06\ M$ *Ans.*

---

* A little later you will learn that the concept of molar concentrations is also important in the calculation of the rate of collision between reacting molecules. See Chapter XIV.

2. What weight of KOH is required to prepare 200 cc. of 5.0 molar solution?

Solution. By definition,

$$M = \frac{\text{Number of moles of solute}}{\text{Number of liters of solution}}$$

Number of moles of solute $= M \times$ Number of liters of solution

$$= 5.0 \times \frac{200}{1000} = 1.0$$

Weight of solute = Number of moles $\times$ Molecular weight

$$= 1.0 \times 56 = 56 \text{ g.} \quad Ans.$$

3. What volume of 2.50 molar $CuSO_4$ solution can be made from 50.0 g. of $CuSO_4$?

Solution. To prepare 1.000 l. of 2.50 molar $CuSO_4$ solution we need

$$2.50 \text{ moles} = 2.50 \times 159.6 \text{ g.} = 399 \text{ g.}$$

Then, .

$$50.0 \text{ g. will make } \frac{50.0}{399} \text{ l.} = 0.125 \text{ l.} \quad Ans.$$

Problems

1. What is the molar concentration of a solution that contains 180 g. of sodium hydroxide per liter? *Ans.* 4.50 *M*.

2. What weight of HCl is required to prepare 800 cc. of 3.00 *M* solution? *Ans.* 87.6 g.

3. What volume of 2.00 molar solution of common salt (NaCl) can be made from 11.7 g. of salt? *Ans.* 100 cc.

4. A solution of zinc chloride contains 43.1 g. of $ZnCl_2$ in 250 cc. of solution. What is the molar concentration?

5. What weight of HNO_3 is required to make 2.5 l. of 3.0 *M* solution?

6. What volume of 1.55 molar sulfuric acid can be prepared from 882 g. of H_2SO_4?

7. What volume of 2.0 *M* sulfuric acid is required to react with 30 g. of NaOH?

8. How many liters of 0.50 molar hydrochloric acid react with 800 cc. of 2.0 molar sodium hydroxide?

THE EQUIVALENT WEIGHTS OF COMPOUNDS

In Chapter II you learned that the equivalent weight of an element is the weight that reacts with 8 grams of oxygen or its equivalent. The equivalent weights of some of the more common elements are:

$$H = 1.008 \qquad Mg = 12.16$$
$$Cl = 35.46 \qquad Al = 8.99$$
$$Na = 23.00$$

As you would expect, the equivalent weight of a compound is defined as the weight of the compound that reacts with one equivalent of anything else (element or compound). To illustrate the use of the definition, we shall calculate the equivalent weights of HCl, H_2SO_4, and H_3PO_4. To do this remember we need only to find the weights of these which react with one equivalent of anything else, element or compound. For convenience, we shall use sodium. The equivalent weight of sodium is the same as its atomic weight. (Why?) Sodium reacts with the acids mentioned above according to the equations:

$$Na + HCl = NaCl + (H)$$
$$2Na + H_2SO_4 = Na_2SO_4 + 2(H)$$
$$3Na + H_3PO_4 = Na_3PO_4 + 3(H)$$

Notice that one-third of a mole of H_3PO_4 reacts with the same amount of sodium as does one-half of a mole of H_2SO_4 or one mole of HCl. These quantities of the three acids are chemically equivalent because they accomplish the same thing, i.e., react with the same amount of sodium and release the same amount of hydrogen. These quantities of the three acids are equivalent weights of the acids because they react with one equivalent weight of sodium. Thus,

Equivalent weight of HCl = Molecular weight = 36.5

Equivalent weight of $H_2SO_4 = \dfrac{\text{Molecular weight}}{2} = \dfrac{98.1}{2} = 49.05$

Equivalent weight of $H_3PO_4 = \dfrac{\text{Molecular weight}}{3} = \dfrac{98.0}{3} = 32.7$

It follows from the definition above that:

1. The gram-equivalent weight of an acid equals the gram-molecular weight of the acid divided by the number of replaceable hydrogen atoms in the molecule of the acid. See illustrations above.

2. The gram-equivalent weight of an hydroxide equals the gram-molecular weight of the hydroxide divided by the number of replaceable hydroxyl groups in the molecule. This is made clear by a consideration of the following reactions.

$$NaOH + HCl = NaCl + H_2O$$
$$Ca(OH)_2 + 2HCl = CaCl_2 + 2H_2O$$
$$Al(OH)_3 + 3HCl = AlCl_3 + 3H_2O$$

We see that 1 gram-molecular weight of NaOH, ½ gram-molecular weight of $Ca(OH)_2$, and ⅓ gram-molecular weight of $Al(OH)_3$ will each separately react with 1 gram-equivalent weight of HCl, and therefore these weights of the hydroxides are their gram-equivalent weights.

3. The equations

$$Na + AgCl = NaCl + Ag$$
$$2Na + CaCl_2 = 2NaCl + Ca$$
$$3Na + AlCl_3 = 3NaCl + Al$$

tell us that 1 gram-equivalent weight of Na reacts with 1 mole of AgCl, ½ mole of $CaCl_2$, and ⅓ mole of $AlCl_3$. These weights of these salts are, therefore, their gram-equivalent weights, since these weights react with one gram-equivalent weight of another substance.

Notice that the gram-equivalent weight of a salt is equal to its gram-molecular weight divided by the total valence of either the positive or the negative group. For example,

Gram-equivalent weight of $MgSO_4$ =

$$\frac{\text{Molecular weight of } MgSO_4}{\text{Valence of Mg}} = \frac{120.38}{2} = 60.19 \text{ g.}$$

Gram-equivalent weight of $Al_2(SO_4)_3$ =

$$\frac{\text{Molecular weight}}{6} = \frac{342.12}{6} = 57.02 \text{ g.}$$

(Bear in mind that conclusions (1), (2), and (3) are not defini-tions; they follow from the general definition above.) *

Let us repeat that the concept of equivalent weights is a most important one. When you have mastered this concept many of your difficulties with problems will disappear. You cannot mas-ter it in a day or week; it must grow familiar by repeated use.

Problems

1. What are the equivalent weights of (*a*) HCl, (*b*) H_2SO_4, (*c*) H_3PO_4, (*d*) NaOH, (*e*) $Ca(OH)_2$, (*f*) $Al(OH)_3$, (*g*) NaCl, (*h*) $CaSO_4$, (*i*) $SnCl_4$, and (*j*) $Al_2(SO_4)_3$?

Ans. (*a*) 36.5, (*b*) 49, (*c*) 32.7, (*d*) 40.0, (*e*) 37.0, (*f*) 26.0, (*g*) 58.5, (*h*) 68.0, (*i*) 65.1, (*j*) 57.0 g.

2. How many gram-equivalent weights of solute are there in 1 l. of one molar solution of the substances above?

Ans. (*a*) 1, (*b*) 2, (*c*) 3, (*d*) 1, (*e*) 2, (*f*) 3, (*g*) 1, (*h*) 2, (*i*) 4, (*j*) 6.

3. Is it true that in any chemical reaction between two substances, *A* and *B*, 1 gram-equivalent weight of *A* reacts with 1 gram-equivalent weight of *B*? Give reasons for your answer.

4. One liter of 1 molar solution of H_2SO_4 (*a*) contains how many gram-equivalent weights of H_2SO_4? (*b*) will react with how many gram-equivalent weights of NaOH? (*c*) will neutralize what volume of 1 molar NaOH solutions?

5. When treated with excess hydrochloric acid, 2.541 g. of zinc liberates 963.66 cc. of hydrogen collected over water at 21° C. and 758 mm. pressure. Calculate the equivalent weight of zinc. *Ans.* 32.7.

6. A 1.00-g. sample of Al is treated with excess dilute sulfuric acid. The hydrogen evolved is collected dry at 20° C. and 745 mm. The equivalent weight of Al is 8.99. What is the volume of the hydrogen?

7. Considering the following reactions.

$$3NaOH + H_3BO_3 = Na_3BO_3 + 3H_2O$$

$$Ca(OH)_2 + H_2F_2 = CaF_2 + 2H_2O$$

$$Ca_3(PO_4)_2 + 3H_2SO_4 = 2H_3PO_4 + 3CaSO_4$$

* These rules do not always apply. For example, in the reaction

$$NaCl + H_2SO_4 = NaHSO_4 + HCl$$

the equivalent weight of H_2SO_4 is equal to its molecular weight. Notice that the definition of equivalent weight still applies, however.

calculate the gram-equivalent weights of H_3BO_3, H_2F_2, and $Ca_3(PO_4)_2$ (a) in terms of gram-molecular weights (for example, the gram-equivalent weight of $H_2SO_4 = \dfrac{\text{g-mol. wt. } H_2SO_4}{2}$ and (b) in terms of grams.

NORMAL SOLUTIONS: NORMALITY

You have learned to express the concentrations of solutions in terms of molarity, i.e., moles, or gram-molecular weights of solutes per liter of solution. We shall now define a more useful unit of concentration. But first let us justify defining a new unit of concentration. Why do we need a new unit? Does not molar concentration serve our purpose? A new unit is not absolutely necessary. It is introduced to shorten our work and clarify our thinking. Consider this. One liter of one molar H_2SO_4 does not react with just 1 liter of one molar NaOH; it reacts with 2. And, in general, equal volumes of solutions of equal molarities do not necessarily react with one another completely. *This new unit of concentration is defined in such a way that equal volumes of solutions of equal concentration (in this unit) exactly neutralize one another.* One gram-molecular weight of H_2SO_4 reacts with two gram-molecular weights of NaOH, but one gram-equivalent weight of H_2SO_4 (or any other substance) reacts with one gram-equivalent weight of NaOH (or any other substance). Therefore, we shall define our new unit, which is called *"normality,"* as *the number of gram-equivalent weights of solute per liter of solution.* Thus a normal solution contains one gram-equivalent weight of solute in a liter of solution, a two-normal solution contains two gram-equivalent weights of solute in a liter of solution, etc.

Illustrative Problems

1. What is the normality of a solution containing 60 g. of NaOH per liter?

Solution. By definition, the normality of a solution is the number of gram-equivalent weights of solute per liter of solution. The gram-equivalent weight of NaOH is 40 g. (The same as its gram-molecular weight.) Therefore,

$$60 \text{ g.} = \frac{60}{40} \text{ g-equiv. wt.} = 1.5 \text{ g-equiv. wt.}$$

and since the volume is 1 l., the normality is 1.5. *Ans.*

2. What weight of H_2SO_4 is required for 600 cc. of 3.00 N solution?

Solution. From the definition of normality, 1 l. of 3.00 N solution requires 3.00 gram-equivalent weights of H_2SO_4; 600 cc. (0.600 l.) of 3.00 N solution requires 0.600×3.00 gram-equivalent weights of H_2SO_4.

$$1 \text{ g-equiv. wt. of } H_2SO_4 = 49.1 \text{ g.}$$

The weight of H_2SO_4 in 600 cc. of 3.00 N solution is

$$0.600 \times 3.00 \times 49.1 = 88.4 \text{ g.} \quad Ans.$$

3. What volume of 2.00 N H_3PO_4 solution can be prepared from 147 g. of H_3PO_4?

Solution. For 1 l. 2.00 N H_3PO_4 we need 2.0 gram-equivalent weights $= 2.00 \times \dfrac{98.0}{3} = 65.3$ g. The 147 g. would make $\dfrac{147}{65.3}$ l. $= 2.25$ l.

We have now discussed two modes of expression of the concentration of solutions in terms of chemical units, the molarity, M, and the normality, N. The question is: Knowing the concentration of a given solution in one of these units, how can we express this concentration in the other unit?

1. Knowing the molar concentration, M, to find the normality, N, multiply M by the number of gram-equivalent weights in one gram-molecular weight of solute. This product is the number of gram-equivalent weights per liter and is, therefore, N, by definition.

2. Knowing N, to find M, divide N by the number of gram-equivalent weights in one gram-molecular weight of solute. This quotient is the number of gram-molecular weights per liter and is, therefore, M.

In general, for a given solution

$$nM = N$$

Where $n =$ number of gram-equivalent weights in one gram-molecular weight of solute (n is always a small whole number: 1, 2, 3, 4, 5, or 6). Notice that the molar concentration, M, of a given solution is never greater than the normality, N. It is equal to N when the gram-equivalent weight is the gram-molecular weight of the solute.

Illustrative Problem

1. What is the normality of a 3 M solution of H_3PO_4?

Solution. A 3 M solution contains, by definition, 3 gram-molecular weights per liter. One gram-molecular weight of H_3PO_4 contains 3 gram-equivalent weights (since the molecule contains 3 replaceable hydrogens); therefore,

$$3 \text{ g-mol. wt. of } H_3PO_4 = 3 \times 3 \text{ g-equiv. wt.}$$

This is in 1 l. of solution, therefore, according to the definition of normality,

$$N = 9 \quad Ans.$$

Problems

1. Calculate the weight of each of the following compounds required to make 1 l. of a one normal solution: $CaCl_2$, $BiCl_3$, NH_4OH, and $HClO_3$.

2. What weight of H_2SO_4 is contained in: (*a*) 25 cc. of 0.9875 N H_2SO_4?   (*b*) 50 cc. of $\dfrac{N}{20}$ H_2SO_4?   *Ans.* (*a*) 1.2 g., (*b*) 0.12 g.

3. What volume of 0.400 N $AgNO_3$ solution can be obtained from 6.795 g. of $AgNO_3$?   *Ans.* 100 cc.

4. What is the molar concentration of a solution containing 65.5 g. of $CaCl_2$ in 600 cc.?   What is the normality of this solution?

5. What weight of HNO_3 is contained in: (*a*) 60 cc. of 0.255 N solution?   (*b*) 40 cc. of 2.734 M solution?

6. What volume of sulfuric acid, having a density of 1.8354 g/cc. and containing 93.19 per cent H_2SO_4 by weight, is necessary to make 100 cc. of 8.00 N acid?   *Ans.* 22.9 cc.

7. Prove that in any dilution of a solution of a compound

$$M \times V = k \quad \text{and} \quad N \times V = k'$$

or

$$M \times V = M' \times V' \quad \text{and} \quad N \times V = N' \times V'$$

What are the units of k and k'?

8. What volume of hydrochloric acid, having a density of 1.2 g/cc. and containing 39.11 per cent HCl, is required to make 1.0 l. of 2.0 N solution?

9. What weight of $Ca(OH)_2$ is required to prepare: (*a*) 1500 cc. of 2.4 M solution?   (*b*) 750 cc. of 0.955 N solution?

10. What volume of 3.5 N solution of Na_2SO_4 can be prepared from 150 g. of Na_2SO_4?

11. What is the normality of a 0.3 M solution of $Fe_2(SO_4)_3$?

NEUTRALIZATION

When an acid reacts with a hydroxide, a salt and water are formed. Such a reaction is given a special name; it is called neutralization. An example of neutralization is the action of sulfuric acid on sodium hydroxide as represented by the equation

$$2NaOH + H_2SO_4 = Na_2SO_4 + 2H_2O$$

In neutralization reactions, the hydrogen atoms of the acid combine with the hydroxyl groups of the hydroxide to form neutral water molecules. Since one hydroxyl group (OH) is equivalent to one hydrogen atom, in any complete neutralization, *the number of equivalents of acid exactly equals the number of equivalents of hydroxide.*

$$N_{\text{hydroxide}} = \frac{\text{Number of gram-equivalent weights of hydroxide}}{\text{Number of liters of solution}} \quad (1)$$

and

$$N_{\text{acid}} = \frac{\text{Number of gram-equivalent weights of acid}}{\text{Number of liters of solution}} \quad (2)$$

Then, from (1) and (2), we get:

$N_{\text{hydroxide}} \times$ Number of liters of hydroxide solution =

Number of gram-equivalent weights of hydroxide   (3)

$N_{\text{acid}} \times$ Number of liters of acid solution =

Number of gram-equivalent weights of acid   (4)

But in a neutralization, the number of gram-equivalent weights of hydroxide equals the number of gram-equivalent weights of acid; therefore,

$N_h \times$ Number of liters of hydroxide solution =

$N_a \times$ Number of liters of acid solution   (5)

Representing *volume in liters* by V, we can rewrite equation 5 in the form

$$N_h \times V_h = N_a \times V_a \qquad (6)$$

When equation 6 is used, the V's can be in any units so long as both are in the same unit. (Why?)

By using equation 6,* we are able to solve all neutralization problems with very little work. Such problems can be solved without the use of equation 6, but the method involves many more steps and thereby increases the chance of error.

Illustrative Problems

1. What volume of 2.0 N NaOH is required to neutralize 300 cc. of 0.50 N H_2SO_4?

Solution. Substituting in the relation

$$N_h \times V_h = N_a \times V_a$$

where V is volume in liters and N is normality, we get

$$2.0 \, V_h = 0.50 \times 0.30$$

$$V_h = \frac{0.50 \times 0.30}{2.0} = 0.075 \, \text{l.} = 75 \, \text{cc. of 2 } N \text{ NaOH}$$

In order to convince yourself of the value of equation 6 and of the usefulness of the method used in its derivation, try working the problem above without using equation 6 or the thought processes involved in its derivation. To do this:

(*a*) Find the weight of H_2SO_4 in the given solution.

(*b*) Using the equation for the reaction, calculate the weight of NaOH that will react with this weight of H_2SO_4.

(*c*) Find the volume of 2.0 N NaOH solution that can be made from this weight of NaOH.

Problems

1. What volume of 1 N H_2SO_4 solution is equivalent to 1 cc. of 1 N HCl?

2. What volume of 0.55 N KOH solution is necessary to neutralize 50 cc. of 1.5 N H_2SO_4 solution? Work two ways.

3. What volume of 0.20 N NaOH solution is necessary to neutralize 100 cc. of 1.2 N H_2SO_4 solution? Work two ways.

* Before using this equation, you should be able to derive it.

4. Prove that when a solution is diluted, although the volume and the normality change, the product $N \times V$ does not change.

5. If 220 cc. of 0.72 N nitric acid is diluted to a volume of 900 cc., what is the new normality?

6. If 200 cc. of 0.25 N NaOH solution is added to 500 cc. of 0.35 N HCl solution, what is the normality of the final solution (a) with respect to HCl and (b) with respect to NaCl?

7. What volume of 0.392 molar H_3PO_4 solution is required to neutralize 1250 cc. of 0.200 N hydroxide?   Work two ways.

8. A 10-cc. sample of sulfuric acid whose density is 1.84 g. per cc. is 93.2 per cent H_2SO_4. What volume of 0.10 N $Ca(OH)_2$ is required to neutralize the acid?

9. What volume of 0.926 N nitric acid is required to neutralize 200 cc. of 0.05 M $Ca(OH)_2$ solution?

10. If 10.0 cc. of 0.903 N HCl requires 8.25 cc. of NaOH solution for neutralization, what is the normality of the NaOH solution?

11. To neutralize 25 cc. of 0.510 N NH_4OH 17 cc. of nitric acid solution is required. What is the normality of the acid? What is its molarity?

GENERAL PROBLEMS BASED ON REACTION EQUATIONS

When two substances, C and D, react with one another, it is true from the very meaning of equivalents that

Number of gram-equivalent weights of C =

Number of gram-equivalent weights of D *   (7)

Remembering the definition of normality, we see that (7) can be written in the form

$$N_C \times V_C = N_D \times V_D \qquad (8)$$

This important general relation, of which equation 6 above is a special case, is directly applicable to all reactions between substances in solution.

Now, if instead of replacing each side of (7) by its equal, $N \times V$, we replace only one, we obtain the expression

$N_C \times V_C$ = Number of gram-equivalent weights of D (9)

---

* This relation of course applies to the amounts of C and D actually reacting and not necessarily to the total amount brought together. For example, two equivalent weights of C could be mixed with one equivalent weight of D, but only one of the equivalent weights of C would react with the one of D.

which is applicable to problems in which the normality of the solution of C and the weight or the volume (in the case of gases) of the other substance, D, is known.

Any problem based on chemical reactions can be solved by the use of (7), (8), or (9). When you are able to use these and understand them, when you no longer consider them as formulas, but as principles, when you are able to "see" them without remembering them, then you have learned one of the most important things that this course is designed to teach.

Illustrative Problems

1. What volume of 2.00 N H_2SO_4 solution is required to react with 5.00 g. of NaOH?

Solution. The gram-equivalent weight of NaOH is 40.0 g.; therefore

$$5.00 \text{ g.} = \frac{5.00}{40.0} \text{ g-equiv. wt. of NaOH}$$

This will react with $\frac{5.00}{40.0}$ g-equiv. wt. of H_2SO_4 (or any other substance with which NaOH reacts). From the definition of normality,

$$\text{Number of gram-equivalent weights} = N \times V$$

where V is in liters

$$\frac{5.00}{40.0} = 2.00V$$

$$V = \frac{5.00}{80.0} = 0.0625 \text{ l.} = 62.5 \text{ cc.} \quad Ans.$$

2. What volume of HCl gas at S.T.P. is required to precipitate all the silver from a solution containing 10.0 g. of $AgNO_3$?

Solution. The equation for the reaction is

$$AgNO_3 + HCl = AgCl + HNO_3$$

Number of gram-equivalent weights of $AgNO_3 = \frac{10.0}{\text{g-equiv. wt.}} = \frac{10.0}{170}$

This will require the same number, $\frac{10.0}{170}$ g-equiv. wt., of HCl. One gram-equivalent weight of HCl occupies 22.4 l. at S.T.P. (since the gram-

equivalent weight of HCl is the same as its gram-molecular weight);
therefore,

$$\text{Volume occupied by } \frac{10.0}{170} \text{ g-equiv. wt.} = \frac{10.0}{170} \times 22.4 = 1.32 \text{ l.} \quad Ans.$$

3. What volume of 1.5 N H_2SO_4 is required to precipitate all the
barium as $BaSO_4$ from 200 cc. of 0.50 N solution of $BaCl_2$?

Solution.

Number of gram-equivalent weights of H_2SO_4

$$= \text{Number of gram-equivalent weights of } BaCl_2$$

Applying the definition of normality, we get,

$$N \times V \text{ of } H_2SO_4 \text{ solution} = N \times V \text{ of } BaCl_2 \text{ solution}$$

$$1.5V = 0.50 \times 200$$

$$V = \frac{0.50 \times 200 \text{ cc.}}{1.5} = 67 \text{ cc.} \quad Ans.$$

Problems

1. In illustrative problems 1, 2, and 3 we used equations 7, 8, and 9.
In which problem was each used?

2. What weight of $BaCl_2$ is needed to precipitate completely $BaSO_4$
from 61.0 cc. of 0.050 N H_2SO_4?　　　　　　　　　*Ans.* 0.318 g.

3. If 79.0 cc. of hydrochloric acid reacts with 1.00 g. of $CaCO_3$, what
is the normality of the acid?　The equation for the reaction is

$$CaCO_3 + 2HCl = CaCl_2 + CO_2 + H_2O \quad Ans. \;\; 0.253 \; N.$$

4. Calculate the volume of hydrochloric acid having a density of 1.2
g/cc. and containing 39 per cent HCl by weight necessary to neutralize
10 cc. of 0.50 N NH_4OH solution.

5. What volume of 2.5 N HCl solution is required to produce 5.6 l. of
Cl_2 (S.T.P.) by the action of manganese dioxide?

6. What volume of 0.50 M H_2SO_4 solution will precipitate all the
barium (as $BaSO_4$) in a solution containing 2.0 g. of $BaCl_2$?

7. What volume of 0.205 N hydrochloric acid will precipitate (as
AgCl) all the silver from a solution containing 1.08 g. of $AgNO_3$?

CHAPTER XIII

RAOULT'S LAW

The vapor pressure of a liquid increases as its temperature is increased. Similarly, the vapor pressure of a solid also increases with rising temperature. At the freezing point, which is the temperature at which the solid and its corresponding liquid are in equilibrium, the vapor pressure of the solid is equal to the vapor pressure of the liquid. If this were not true the solid and liquid would not be in equilibrium. The freezing point of water is 0° C.; at this temperature both water and ice have a vapor pressure of 4.6 mm. A sketch of the vapor pressure of a solid and liquid is shown in the diagram. The dotted line CB represents the vapor

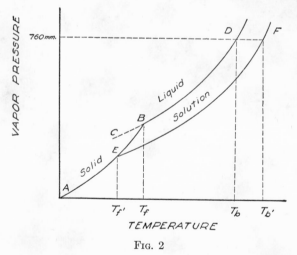

Fig. 2

pressure of the supercooled liquid. T_f is the freezing point and T_b is the standard boiling point of the pure liquid, i.e., the temperature at which its vapor pressure is equal to the external pressure, 760 mm.

By experiment it has been found that when a solute is dissolved in a liquid, the vapor pressure of the liquid is lowered. If the solute is non-volatile the vapor pressure of the solution is that of the solvent. This is represented by the curve EF on the diagram. From this diagram we see why the boiling point of the solution T_B' is higher than that of the pure solvent, and the freezing point of the solution T_f' is lower than that of the pure solvent.

Experiments show that when one mole of a non-volatile non-electrolyte is added to 1000 grams of water, the boiling point is raised 0.52° C. This elevation is known as the molal boiling-point elevation constant for water. Each solvent has its own molal (1 gram-molecular weight of solute per 1000 grams of solvent) boiling-point elevation constant. These constants for a few of the more important solvents are given in a table at the end of this chapter.

This quantitative relation between the moles of solute and the weight of the solvent furnishes a convenient method for the determination of molecular weights. Or, if the molecular weight is known, the weight of solute required to produce any desired increase in the boiling point can be calculated.

Illustrative Problems

1. A 3.00-g. sample of a non-electrolyte when dissolved in 10.0 g. of water gives a boiling point of 101.04° C. at 760 mm. What is the molecular weight of the compound?

Solution.

The boiling point of water at 760 mm. = 100.00° C.

Increase in boiling point = 101.04 − 100.00 = 1.04° C.

1 mole solute in 1000 g. water increases boiling point 0.52° C.

Then,

$$\text{Moles solute per 1000 g. water} = \frac{1.04}{0.52} = 2$$

Now we know that for every 1000 g. of solvent we have 2 moles of solute. If 10.0 g. of water contains 3.00 g. of solute,

$$1 \text{ g. water contains } \frac{3.00}{10.00} \text{ g. of solute}$$

$$1000 \text{ g. water contains } \frac{3.00}{10.00} \times 1000 = 300 \text{ g. solute}$$

Therefore,

$$2 \text{ moles} = 300 \text{ g.}$$

$$1 \text{ mole} \ = 150 \text{ g.} \quad Ans.$$

2. What weight of cane sugar, $C_{12}H_{22}O_{11}$, is necessary to raise the boiling point of 50 g. of water 0.10° C.?
Solution.

Molecular weight of cane sugar = 342

342 g. sugar will raise the boiling point of 1000 g. water 0.52° C.

$342 \times \dfrac{0.10}{0.52}$ g. sugar raises the boiling point of 1000 g. water 0.10° C.

Then,

$$1000 \text{ g. water contains } \frac{342 \times 0.10}{0.52} \text{ g. sugar}$$

$$1 \text{ g. water contains } \frac{342 \times 0.10}{0.52 \times 1000} \text{ g. sugar}$$

$$50 \text{ g. water contains } \frac{342 \times 0.10}{0.52 \times 1000} \times 50 = 3.3 \text{ g. sugar} \quad Ans.$$

THE LOWERING OF THE FREEZING POINT

Actual experiments show that the lowering of the freezing point is proportional to the number of moles of solute in a given weight of solvent. Just as in the case of the elevation of the boiling point, it is customary to express the concentration of the solution in gram-molecular weights (moles) of solute per 1000 g. of solvent. One mole of a non-ionizing substance when dissolved in 1000 g. of water lowers its freezing point 1.86° C. Other molal freezing-point lowering constants are given at the end of the chapter.

The lowering of the freezing point has some distinct advantages over the elevation of the boiling point as a method for the determination of molecular weights. We are all familiar with the fact that a slight change in atmospheric pressure appreciably changes the boiling point of a solution; hence, in measuring boiling point elevations, it is necessary to compensate for slight changes in atmospheric pressure. However, the freezing point of a liquid is not appreciably altered by slight changes in pressure; hence, no correction is necessary.

Illustrative Problems

1. When 2.00 g. of a certain compound is dissolved in 25.0 g. of water the freezing point is lowered 1.25° C. What is the molecular weight of the compound?

Solution.

$$25.0 \text{ g. solvent contains } 2.00 \text{ g. solute}$$

$$1 \text{ g. solvent contains } \frac{2.00}{25.0} \text{ g. solute}$$

Then,

$$1000 \text{ g. solvent contains } \frac{2.00}{25.0} \times 1000 = 80.0 \text{ g. solute}$$

The freezing point lowering is 1.25° C. If the solution had contained one mole per 1000 g. of H_2O, the freezing-point lowering would have been 1.86° C. From this we see that the solution contains less than one mole per 1000 g. of water.

$$\text{Moles solute per 1000 g. } H_2O = \frac{1.25}{1.86} \text{ moles}$$

Then

$$\frac{1.25}{1.86} \times \text{Gram-molecular weight of solute} = 80 \text{ g.}$$

$$\text{Gram-molecular weight of solute} = 80 \times \frac{1.86}{1.25} = 119 \text{ g.}$$

Or

$$\text{Molecular weight} = 119 \quad Ans.$$

2. What weight of alcohol, C_2H_6O, is necessary to lower the freezing point of 2500 g. of water 3.00° C.?

Solution.

$$\text{Molecular weight of } C_2H_6O = 46.0$$

One mole solute per 1000 g. H_2O lowers the freezing point 1.86° C. The number of moles of solute per 1000 g. H_2O required to lower the freezing point 3.00° C. $= \dfrac{3.00}{1.86}$ moles. The weight of solute per 1000 g. solvent required to lower the freezing point 3.00° C. $= \dfrac{3.00}{1.86} \times 46.0$ g. The weight of solute per 1 g. solvent required to lower the freezing point

$3.00° C. = \dfrac{3.00}{1.86} \times \dfrac{46.0}{1000}$ g. The weight of solute per 2500 g. solvent required to lower the freezing point 3.00° C. is:

$$\frac{3.00}{1.86} \times \frac{46.0}{1000} \times 2500 = 185 \text{ g.} \quad Ans.$$

DETERMINATION OF DEGREE OF IONIZATION

It has already been shown that for substances which do not ionize the elevation of the boiling point and the lowering of the freezing point are proportional to the number of molecules of solute dissolved in a given weight of solvent. In other words, for a given weight of solvent the change in the boiling point or freezing point is determined by the number of dissolved particles. If we dissolve 1 mole of some electrolyte, say NaCl, in 1000 grams water, the number of particles of solute will be greater than the number of molecules dissolved, because of the dissociation of part of the molecules into ions. Each molecule of NaCl that ionized gives two ions. Thus, if we dissolve 1 mole of NaCl in water and α is the fraction of molecules of NaCl which ionize, we shall have $(1 + \alpha)$ moles of particles at equilibrium. This can be seen by referring to the illustration shown below.

$$NaCl \leftrightarrows Na^+ + Cl^-$$

Number moles NaCl at equilibrium $= 1 - \alpha$, where the number of moles of NaCl ionizing $= \alpha$. For each molecule of NaCl which ionizes we get one Na^+ and one Cl^-.

Then, $$\text{Moles } Na^+ = \alpha$$

$$\text{Moles } Cl^- = \alpha$$

The total moles of particles in solution $= (1 - \alpha) + \alpha + \alpha = 1 + \alpha$.

If the NaCl were completely ionized, we should have twice as many particles in solution as there are molecules of NaCl dissolved. Under this condition, 1 mole of NaCl dissolved in 1000 grams of water would lower the freezing point $2 \times 1.86°$ C. Actually, complete ionization occurs only in very dilute solutions.

From this we see that the freezing-point lowering of a 1 molal sodium chloride solution is more than $1.86°$ C. but less than $2 \times 1.86°$ C. In fact it is $(1 + \alpha)1.86°$ C.

The lowering of the freezing-point or the elevation of the boiling point may be conveniently used to calculate the degree of ionization for solutions of electrolytes.

Illustrative Problems

1. A solution containing 1.50 g. KCl in 100 g. H_2O freezes at $-0.684°$ C. What is the degree of ionization of the KCl?

Solution.

100 g. H_2O contains 1.50 g. KCl

1000 g. H_2O would contain 15.0 g. KCl

1000 g. H_2O would contain $\dfrac{15.0}{74.6} = 0.201$ mole KCl

But part of the KCl is ionized. Let $x =$ moles KCl which are ionized. Then $x =$ moles $K^+ =$ moles Cl^-, and $0.201 - x =$ moles KCl which have not ionized.

$$KCl \quad \leftrightarrows \quad K^+ + Cl^-$$
$$0.201 - x \quad\quad x \quad\quad x$$

Total moles of dissolved particles $= (0.201 - x) + x + x = (0.201 + x)$ moles.

From every mole of dissolved particles per 1000 g. H_2O we shall have a lowering of $1.86°$ C. Then the product of the total number of moles per 1000 g. $H_2O \times 1.86$ must be equal to the actual lowering of the freezing point. Or,

$$(0.201 + x)1.86 = 0.684$$

$$x = \frac{0.684}{1.86} - 0.201$$

$$x = 0.167 \text{ mole}$$

We now see that 0.167 mole out of 0.201 mole of KCl is ionized.

$$\text{Per cent ionization} = \frac{0.167}{0.201} \times 100 = 83.1 \quad Ans.$$

2. A solution contains 3.0 g. of $CaCl_2$ in 50 g. of water. If the $CaCl_2$ is 75 per cent ionized, what is the freezing point of the solution?
Solution.

50 g. water contains 3.0 g. $CaCl_2$

1 g. water contains $\dfrac{3.0}{50}$ g. $CaCl_2$

1000 g. water contains $\dfrac{3.0}{50} \times 1000 = 60$ g. $CaCl_2$

The molecular weight of $CaCl_2 = 111$

Moles of $CaCl_2$ per 1000 g. water $= \dfrac{60}{111} = 0.54$

But, 0.75 of the $CaCl_2$ molecules are ionized.

Moles $CaCl_2$ ionized $= 0.54 \times 0.75 = 0.405$

Moles $CaCl_2$ not ionized $= 0.54 - 0.405 = 0.135$

Now, if we look at the equation below, we see that the number of moles of Ca^{++} equals the number of moles of $CaCl_2$ that ionized, and the number of moles of Cl^- equals twice the number of moles of $CaCl_2$ that ionized.

$$CaCl_2 \;\leftrightarrows\; CaCl_2 \;+\; Ca^{++} \;+\; 2Cl^-$$

| | 0.135 | 0.405 | 2×0.405 |
| original sample | un-ionized portion | ionized portion | |

Thus, it is seen that at equilibrium:

Moles of $CaCl_2 = 0.135$

Moles of $Ca^{++} = 0.405$

Moles of $Cl^- = 2 \times 0.405 = 0.810$

Total moles per 1000 g. of water $= 0.135 + 0.405 + 0.810 = 1.35$

For each mole of solute per 1000 g. water, the freezing point is lowered 1.86° C.

Lowering for 1.35 moles per 1000 g. water $= 1.35 \times 1.86 = 2.5$°C.

The freezing point of the solution is 2.5° C. lower than the freezing point of pure water which is 0° C.

Freezing point of solution $= 0.0 - 2.5 = -2.5$° C. *Ans.*

Solvent	Molal B.P. Elevation	Molal F.P. Lowering
Water	0.52°	1.86°
Benzene	2.57°	4.90°
Nitrobenzene	5.02°	7.00°
Acetic Acid	2.7°	3.90°

Problems

1. When 2.00 g. of a certain non-electrolyte is dissolved in 40.0 g. of water the freezing-point lowering is 3.29° C. What is the molecular weight of the compound?   *Ans.* 28.3.

2. The boiling point of pure benzene is 80.2° C. What is the boiling point of a solution of 13.0 g. of $C_{10}H_8$ (naphthalene, a non-electrolyte) in 200 g. benzene?   *Ans.* 81.5° C.

3. What weight of glucose, $C_6H_{12}O_6$, must be added to 1500 g. H_2O to make it freeze at −5.25° C.?

4. The freezing point of a solution containing 20 g. of a non-electrolyte in 150 g. nitrobenzene is 2.7° C. The freezing point of nitrobenzene is 5.7° C. What is the molecular weight of the compound?   *Ans.* 311.

5. A solution containing 8.5 g. $AgNO_3$ in 50 g. water freezes at −3.35° C. What is the degree of ionization of the $AgNO_3$? *Ans.* 80%.

6. If a 2.0 molal NaCl solution is 86 per cent ionized, what is its boiling point?   *Ans.* 101.9° C.

7. An automobile radiator holds 20 qt. How many pints of ethylene glycol, $C_2H_6O_2$, must be added so that the freezing point will be 10° F.? Consider that there will be no volume change on mixing the ethylene glycol and water. The density of ethylene glycol is 1.12 g/cc.

CHAPTER XIV

EQUILIBRIUM

REACTION RATE AND THE LAW OF MASS ACTION

Frequently the speed with which a reaction occurs is more important than the chemical composition of the products formed. For example, in the decomposition of an explosive such as TNT we are not nearly so much interested in the products as we are in the rate of formation of these products. There are many reactions which the chemist would like to speed up. An example is the fermentation of grain into alcohol. There are other reactions which we should like to retard. An example is the rusting of iron and steel. Thus you see that it is a matter of great practical importance to know the factors which affect reaction rates.

The factors which determine the rate of reaction are:

1. The nature of the reacting substances. For example, sodium and chlorine tend to react rapidly whereas lead and oxygen tend to react relatively slowly. Of course, once a given reaction has been chosen for a rate study, this factor is fixed.

2. The temperature. With very few exceptions, a rise in temperature increases the rate of reaction. The quantitative relation between reaction rate and temperature is not a simple one and will not be discussed here, but you should remember that, in general, reaction rates increase rapidly with rising temperature. For example, a certain reaction that requires 20 minutes at 25° C. requires only 5 sec. at 100° C.

3. The catalyst. As you recall, a catalyst is a substance which alters the speed of a reaction without being consumed. Often the effect of a catalyst is enormous. For example, hydrogen and oxygen do not react with measurable speed at room temperature without a catalyst, but when these gases are brought in contact with finely divided platinum, they combine with explosive violence.

4. Concentration of reacting substances. In order for two molecules to react, they must come into contact or must collide. When the concentration of reacting molecules is increased, the

collision rate is increased, and therefore the reaction rate is increased. The quantitative relation between reaction rate and concentration was discovered experimentally in 1867 by two Scandinavian investigators, Guldberg and Waage. This relation is called the *law of mass action*. This law states that [*at a given temperature the speed of a chemical reaction is directly proportional to the concentrations of the reacting substances.*] Thus, for the general reaction

$$A + B = C + D \tag{1}$$

the speed is directly proportional to the concentration of A and to the concentration of B. This can be expressed in symbols thus:

$$\text{Speed} \propto [A] \times [B] \quad \text{or} \quad \text{Speed} = k[A] \times [B] \tag{2}$$

where $[A]$ = concentration of $[A]$ in moles per liter and k is the proportionality constant,* called the *specific reaction rate constant* because it is numerically equal to the speed of the reaction when the concentrations of A and B are both unity. The numerical value of this constant depends on the mutual affinity of A and B and also on the temperature.

Reaction speed is usually expressed in moles per unit volume per unit time, usually moles per liter per sec. or moles per liter per minutes.

APPLICATION OF THE LAWS OF MASS ACTION TO REVERSIBLE REACTIONS

Consider the general reversible reaction

$$A + B \leftrightarrows C + D$$

This is really a combination of two reactions: $A + B \rightarrow C + D$, and the reverse $C + D \rightarrow A + B$. We shall refer to these as reactions 1 and 2 respectively. Then by the law of mass action

$$\text{Speed}_1 \propto [A] \times [B] \quad \text{or} \quad \text{Speed}_1 = k_1[A] \times [B] \tag{3}$$

and

$$\text{Speed}_2 \propto [C] \times [D] \quad \text{or} \quad \text{Speed}_2 = k_2[C] \times [D] \tag{4}$$

---

* Two things are said to be proportional when one is equal to a constant times the other. For example, the cost of a tankful of gasoline is proportional to the number of gallons, or

$$\text{Cost} = k \times \text{Number of gallons}$$

The constant of proportionality here is the cost per gallon.

At equilibrium these two speeds must be equal; therefore,

$$k_1[A] \times [B] = k_2[C] \times [D] \tag{5}$$

or

$$\frac{[C] \times [D]}{[A] \times [B]} = \frac{k_1}{k_2} = K_{\text{eq.}} \tag{6}$$

Obviously this relation 6 is true only at equilibrium. $K_{\text{eq.}}$ is known as the equilibrium constant. By convention the products of the reaction as written appear in the numerator of the equilibrium constant expression.

Illustrative Problem

1. Alcohol and acetic acid react according to the equation

$$C_2H_5OH + H \cdot C_2H_3O_2 \leftrightarrows C_2H_5 \cdot C_2H_3O_2 + H_2O$$

When one mole of alcohol and one of acetic acid are mixed at room temperature, $\frac{2}{3}$ mole of ester ($C_2H_5 \cdot C_2H_3O_2$) and $\frac{2}{3}$ mole of water are formed at equilibrium. Calculate (*a*) the equilibrium constant and (*b*) the number of moles of ester that can be formed by this reaction at room temperature from 2 moles of alcohol and 1 mole of acid.

Solution. (*a*) For this reaction

$$K_{\text{eq.}} = \frac{[C_2H_5 \cdot C_2H_3O_2][H_2O]}{[C_2H_5 \cdot OH][H \cdot C_2H_3O_2]}$$

In order to obtain the numerical value of this constant we need only find the equilibrium values of the concentrations, and substitute these in the above expression. From the data above, at equilibrium

$$[C_2H_5 \cdot C_2H_3O_2] = [H_2O] = \frac{\frac{2}{3}}{V}$$

where V = volume in liters of the mixture at equilibrium

$$[C_2H_5 \cdot OH] = [H \cdot C_2H_3O_2] = \frac{1 - \frac{2}{3}}{V} = \frac{\frac{1}{3}}{V}$$

Then

$$K_{\text{eq.}} = \frac{\left(\frac{\frac{2}{3}}{V}\right)^2}{\left(\frac{\frac{1}{3}}{V}\right)^2} = \frac{(\frac{2}{3})^2}{(\frac{1}{3})^2} = 4.0 \quad Ans.$$

(b) Let X = the number of moles of ester formed from 2.0 moles of alcohol and 1.0 mole of acid.

Then at equilibrium

$$[C_2H_5 \cdot C_2H_3O_2] = [H_2O] = \frac{X}{V}$$

$$[C_2H_5OH] = \frac{2.0 - X}{V}$$

$$[H \cdot C_2H_3O_2] = \frac{1.0 - X}{V}$$

These concentrations must satisfy the equilibrium constant expression; therefore

$$K_{eq.} = 4 = \frac{[C_2H_5 \cdot C_2H_3O_2][H_2O]}{[C_2H_5OH][H \cdot C_2H_3O_2]}$$

$$= \frac{\left(\dfrac{X}{V}\right)^2}{\left(\dfrac{2.0 - X}{V}\right)\left(\dfrac{1.0 - X}{V}\right)} = \frac{X^2}{(2.0 - X)(1.0 - X)} = \frac{X^2}{2 - 3X + X^2}$$

Then,

$$4(2 - 3X + X^2) = X^2$$

$$8 - 12X + 4X^2 = X^2$$

$$3X^2 - 12X + 8 = 0$$

$$X = \frac{12 - \sqrt{144 - 96}}{6} = \frac{12 - \sqrt{48}}{6} = \frac{12 - 6.93}{6} = 0.84 \quad Ans.$$

Notice the increase in yield due to the excess of alcohol.

Problems

1. How much ester $(C_2H_5 \cdot C_2H_3O_2)$ will be formed when 1.0 mole of alcohol, 2.0 moles of acetic acid, and 3.0 moles of water are mixed and allowed to come to equilibrium at room temperature? *Ans.* 0.60 mole.

2. Hydrogen and iodine react according to the equation

$$H_2 + I_2 = 2HI$$

When 8.0 moles of H_2 and 3.0 moles of I_2 are mixed and allowed to come to equilibrium at a certain high temperature, 5.6 moles of HI is formed. Calculate (a) the equilibrium constant, and (b) the number of moles of HI that will be formed at equilibrium from 8.0 moles of H_2 and 6.0 moles of I_2.

IONIZATION CONSTANTS

If the reversible reaction is an ionization like

$$NH_4OH \leftrightarrows NH_4^+ + OH^-$$

then by (6)

$$\frac{[NH_4^+] \times [OH^-]}{[NH_4OH]} = K_i$$

where the general equilibrium constant K_{eq}. has been replaced by K_i, *the ionization constant.*

Illustrative Example

At 25° C., NH_4OH is 1.3 per cent ionized in a 0.10 N solution. Calculate (a) its ionization constant and (b) its percentage ionization in 1.0 N solution.

Solution. (a) The equation for the ionization is

$$NH_4OH \leftrightarrows NH_4^+ + OH^-$$

$$[OH^-] = [NH_4^+] = 1.3\% \text{ of } 0.10 = 0.013 \times 0.10 = 0.0013 \text{ moles/l.}$$

$$[NH_4OH] = 0.10 - 0.0013 = 0.10 *$$

Therefore,

$$\frac{[NH_4^+] \times [OH^-]}{[NH_4OH]} = K_i = \frac{(0.0013)^2}{0.10} = 1.7 \times 10^{-5} \quad Ans.$$

(b) Let α equal the fraction of the NH_4OH ionized in 1.0 N solution. Then,

$$\alpha = [OH^-] = [NH_4^+] \text{ in the 1 } N \text{ sol. of ammonium hydroxide}$$

$$1 - \alpha = [NH_4OH]$$

Now we know that $\alpha < 0.013$ because 0.013 is the fraction ionized in 0.10 N solution and the percentage ionization decreases with increasing concentration. Then for the number of significant figures which we have here, $1.0 - \alpha$ is essentially equal to 1.0. Then,

$$[NH_4OH] = 1.0$$

* Consider the number of significant figures.

And since

$$\frac{[NH_4^+] \times [OH^-]}{[NH_4OH]} = K_i = 1.7 \times 10^{-5}$$

$$\frac{\alpha^2}{1.0} = 1.7 \times 10^{-5}$$

$$\alpha = \sqrt{1.7 \times 10^{-5}} = \sqrt{17 \times 10^{-6}} = \sqrt{17} \times 10^{-3} = 0.0041$$

Per cent ionization = 0.41   *Ans.*

Notice how much less the percentage ionization is in this more concentrated solution.

Problems

1. (*a*) What is the concentration of the hydrogen ion in a 0.01 N solution of acetic acid which is 4.2 per cent ionized?   (*b*) What is the ionization constant of the acid?   (*c*) What is the percentage ionization in a 0.080 N solution?   *Ans.* (*c*) 1.5%.

2. In 0.10 N solution, HF is 7.0 per cent ionized. Calculate the ionization constant of this acid.

3. Hydrocyanic acid is only 0.01 per cent ionized in 0.1 M solution. Calculate (*a*) its ionization constant, and (*b*) the concentration of H^+ in a 0.5 M solution of this acid.

4. The ionization constant of ammonium hydroxide is 1.8×10^{-5}. Calculate the concentration of hydroxyl ion in the following solutions, (*a*) 1.0 N, (*b*) 0.10 N, and (*c*) 0.01 N.

SOLUBILITY PRODUCT PRINCIPLE

It has been found by experiment that at a given temperature in a *saturated solution* of a *slightly soluble electrolyte* the product of the molar concentrations of the ions is a constant. This is known as the solubility product principle, and the constant is the solubility product constant.

Silver chloride is a slightly soluble electrolyte. When an excess of AgCl is added to water, the following equilibria are set up.

$$AgCl \leftrightarrows AgCl \leftrightarrows Ag^+ + Cl^-$$
solid   in
solution

and in this saturated solution

$$[Ag^+] \times [Cl^-] = L_{AgCl}$$

where L_{AgCl} is the solubility product constant of AgCl. (Some authors use the symbol $K_{S.P.\ AgCl}$ for this constant.)

The solubility product principle is useful in explaining (a) the formation of precipitates and (b) the dissolving of precipitates.

PRECIPITATION

It is often said that when Cl^- and Ag^+ are brought together in solution, a precipitate of AgCl is formed. This statement is not necessarily true, because according to the solubility product principle a precipitate will form only if the concentration of the Ag^+ times the concentration of the Cl^- exceeds the solubility product constant of AgCl, i.e., in order for AgCl to precipitate,

$$[Ag^+]\,[Cl^-] > L_{AgCl}\ (1.5 \times 10^{-10})$$

Whenever Ag^+ and Cl^- are brought together in solution so that

$$[Ag^+]\,[Cl^-] > L_{AgCl}$$

AgCl will precipitate (unless the solution becomes supersaturated) until

$$[Ag^+]\,[Cl^-] = L_{AgCl}$$

The solution will then be saturated with AgCl and no more will precipitate without a change in conditions.

The illustration above is an example of the application of the general rule that in order to precipitate the slightly soluble electrolyte AB (which ionizes thus: $AB \leftrightharpoons A^+ + B^-$) it is necessary that

$$[A^+]\,[B^-] > L_{AB}$$

Solution of Precipitates. Having considered above the conditions necessary in the formation of precipitates, let us consider now the reverse problem, that of dissolving precipitates.

Silver chloride is said to be insoluble in water. Actually it is soluble to the extent of 0.0018 g/l. at 25° C. This solubility corresponds to a solubility product constant of 1.5×10^{-10} (check!). If AgCl is added to water, enough of it will dissolve to make

$$[Ag^+]\,[Cl^-] = L_{AgCl}\ (1.5 \times 10^{-10})$$

If, now, to this saturated solution something that reduces the concentration of either the Ag^+ or the Cl^- is added

$$[Ag^+][Cl^-] < L_{AgCl}$$

and the solution will be unsaturated. But more solid AgCl will dissolve in the unsaturated solution in an attempt to saturate the solution and will make

$$[Ag^+] \times [Cl^-] = L_{AgCl}$$

Silver chloride can be dissolved by the use of ammonia. Silver chloride is insoluble in water, but it is quite soluble in ammonia solution, because the concentration of the Ag^+ is reduced by the reaction

$$Ag^+ + 2NH_3 = Ag(NH_3)_2{}^+$$

In general, in order to dissolve an "insoluble" precipitate, we need only add a reagent that will in some way * reduce the concentration of one of the ions. Summary: For the slightly soluble electrolyte AB,

If $[A^+] \times [B^-] = L_{AB}$, the solution is saturated.

If $[A^+] \times [B^-] > L_{AB}$, the solution is supersaturated and a precipitate of AB will form.

If $[A^+] \times [B^-] < L_{AB}$, the solution is unsaturated and AB will dissolve in this solution.

Illustrative Problems

1. The solubility of AgI is 3.0×10^{-6} g/l. Calculate its solubility product constant.

Solution.

$$[Ag^+] \times [I^-] = L_{AgI}$$

$$3.0 \times 10^{-6} \text{ g/l. AgI} = \frac{3.0 \times 10^{-6}}{235} \text{ mole/l.} = 1.3 \times 10^{-8} \text{ mole/l.}$$

---

* In the case of AgCl above, the concentration of the Ag^+ was reduced by the formation of the complex ion $Ag(NH_3)_2{}^+$. Often the concentration of an ion is reduced by the formation, with another ion, of a practically un-ionized substance such as water.

In such a dilute solution we may assume complete ionization; therefore

$$[Ag^+] = [I^-] = 1.3 \times 10^{-8} \text{ mole/l.}$$

and

$$[Ag^+] \times [I^-] = L_{AgI} = (1.3 \times 10^{-8})^2 = 1.7 \times 10^{-16} \quad Ans.$$

Problems

1. The solubility of $MgCO_3$ is 5.0×10^{-3} mole/l. Assume complete ionization and calculate its solubility product constant.

Ans. 2.5×10^{-5}.

2. The solubility of $BaSO_4$ is 2.5×10^{-3} g/l. Calculate its solubility product constant. *Ans.* 1.1×10^{-10}.

3. The solubility product constant of AgCl is 1.5×10^{-10}. Assuming 100 per cent ionization, calculate the solubility of AgCl in (a) moles per liter and (b) grams per liter.

4. The solubility of $PbSO_4$ is 4.18 g/l. What is the solubility product constant of this salt?

5. The solubility product constant of CdS is 1.4×10^{-28}. Calculate its solubility in (a) moles per liter and (b) molecules per cubic centimeter.

6. The solubility product constant of HgS is 3×10^{-53}. One molecule of HgS will saturate what volume of water?

7. The solubility product constant of $PbSO_4$ is 1.8×10^{-8}. At room temperature the solubility of $PbCl_2$ is 7.0 g/l. If 100 cc. of a saturated solution of $PbCl_2$ is mixed with 50 cc. of 1.0 M H_2SO_4, will $PbSO_4$ precipitate? Justify your answer.

THE COMMON ION EFFECT

The solubility of AgI in water is 1.3×10^{-8} mole/l. Is its solubility the same in a solution containing KI? A little thought should convince you that AgI is less soluble in the KI solution, because the excess I^- tends to drive the reaction

$$\underset{\text{solid}}{AgI} \leftrightarrows \underset{\substack{\text{in} \\ \text{solution}}}{AgI} \leftrightarrows Ag^+ + I^-$$

to the left. The iodide ion is *common* to the two electrolytes. The iodide ion from the KI has an *effect* on the solubility of the AgI. This is an example of the common ion effect.

A more important example of this effect is illustrated in the following example. Acetic acid, represented as HAc, ionizes thus

$$HAc \leftrightarrows H^+ + Ac^-$$

The ionization constant of this acid is 1.8×10^{-5}, i.e.,

$$\frac{[H^+] \times [Ac^-]}{[HAc]} = 1.8 \times 10^{-5} \tag{8}$$

In a 0.10 N solution, the HAc is 1.3 per cent ionized (show this!), and therefore $[H^+] = 0.0013$ mole/l. Calculate the $[H^+]$ in a solution which is 0.10 N in HAc and also 0.10 N in NaAc. Assume the NaAc to be 100 per cent ionized.

It is apparent without any calculation that the $[H^+]$ will be less than it was in water solution above, because the great excess of Ac^- from the NaAc will suppress the ionization of the weak acid. Now regardless of what is in the solution with the acetic acid, equation 8 must be satisfied.

Let α = fraction of HAc ionized.
Then,

$$[H^+] = 0.10\alpha$$

$$[Ac^-] = 0.10 + 0.10\alpha = 0.10(1 + \alpha)$$

$$[HAc] = 0.10 - 0.10\alpha = 0.10(1 - \alpha)$$

But when we consider that $\alpha < 0.013$ (why?) and that we are using only two significant figures, then

$$[Ac^-] = 0.10 \quad \text{and} \quad [HAc] = 0.10$$

and, on substituting in (8),

$$\frac{(0.10\alpha)(0.10)}{(0.10)} = 0.10\alpha = 1.8 \times 10^{-5} = [H^+]$$

Notice the great decrease in the concentration of the hydrogen ion due to the presence of a large excess of acetate ions.

Problems

1. What would be the concentration of the H^+ ion in a liter of solution made by dissolving 12 g. of HAc and 16.4 g. of NaAc? $K = 1.8 \times 10^{-5}$

2. If 26.8 g. of NH_4Cl is dissolved in 500 cc. of 1.0 M NH_4OH solution, what is the concentration of the OH^-? State all assumptions.

3. What is the concentration of H^+ in a solution which contains 10 g. NaCN in 100 cc. of 0.50 M HCN solution?

4. What weight of silver chloride is soluble in 100 cc. of 1.0 M sodium chloride solution?

5. What weight of NH_4Cl must be added to 200 cc. of 1.0 M NH_4OH in order that the concentration of the OH^- be 10^{-4}?

6. What weight of NH_4Cl must be added to 100 cc. of 0.3 M magnesium chloride to prevent $Mg(OH)_2$ from precipitating when the solution is made 0.5 M with NH_4OH? The solubility product constant of $Mg(OH)_2$ is 5.5×10^{-12}.

REVIEW PROBLEMS

Heretofore, we have been almost entirely concerned with simple types of problems, such as combining weights, valence, and normality of solutions. Actual practical problems can, however, seldom be classified under a single simple type; they usually involve a combination of two or more types. It is with such problems that we shall henceforth be concerned.

In working these problems be sure to remember:

1. The four requirements for a perfect solution of a problem. If you have forgotten these, you can find them in the introduction.

2. Significant figures.

3. To look back over the problem and work it roughly in your head in order to see if your answer is possibly correct.

. . . .

I. Density (Specific Gravity) and Percentage

1. What weight of an iron alloy containing 24.0 per cent manganese must be added to 1867 lb. of iron to obtain an alloy containing 2.00 per cent Mn?

2. What volume of 90.0 per cent sulfuric acid having a density of 1.8144 g/cc. is required to make 500 cc. of 30.0 per cent sulfuric acid of density 1.2185 g/cc.?

3. What volume of ammonium hydroxide solution having a density of 0.924 g/cc. and containing 20.5 per cent NH_3 by weight contains 15.0 g. of NH_3?

4. What weight of HNO_3 is contained in 1.00 cc. of nitric acid having a specific gravity of 1.20 and containing 32.36 per cent HNO_3?

5. What volume of the nitric acid in problem 4 must be added to 500 g. of water to give a solution containing 10.0 per cent HNO_3?

6. What volume of 40.1 per cent hydrochloric acid having a density of 1.21 g/cc. is required to make 500 cc. of 30.0 per cent hydrochloric acid whose density is 1.15 g/cc.?

7. Hydrochloric acid whose specific gravity is 1.200 contains 39.86 per cent HCl. A 50.00-cc. sample of this acid is diluted to 250.00 cc. What volume of the diluted acid contains 2.000 g. of HCl?

8. Sodium hydroxide solution whose specific gravity is 1.383 contains 35.0 per cent NaOH. What volume of this solution contains 8 00 g. of NaOH?

II. Percentage Composition and Equivalent Weight

9. One of the oxides of nitrogen is 53.33 per cent oxygen. What is the equivalent weight of nitrogen in the oxide?

10. In another oxide the equivalent weight of nitrogen is 4.67. What is the percentage of nitrogen in this oxide?

11. Copper has an equivalent weight of 31.8. What is the percentage of chlorine in cupric chloride?

12. A metal has an equivalent weight of 27.295. What weight of this metal is necessary to prepare 300 g. of its chloride?

13. A metal has an equivalent weight of 20.0. What is the percentage of chlorine in the metallic chloride?

14. A metallic oxide is found to contain 22.27 per cent oxygen. This same metal forms a telluride containing 69.55 per cent tellurium. What is the equivalent weight of tellurium?

III. Gas Laws and Molecular Weights

15. If 0.460 g. of a certain compound occupies a volume of 250 cc. at 25° C. and 740 mm., what is the molecular weight of this compound?

16. Methane, a gaseous compound, has a molecular weight of 16.0. What volume is occupied by 1.00 g. of methane at 27° C. and 900 mm.?

17. What volume is occupied by 1.00 g. of N_2, if the gas is collected over water at 25° C. and a total pressure of 740 mm.?

18. What is the molecular weight of a gas 0.160 g. of which occupies a volume of 42.5 cc. when collected over water at 22° C. and 740 mm. barometric pressure?

19. Calculate the molecular weight of a gas 3.128 g. of which occupies a volume of 2.820 l. when collected over water at 22° C. and 755 mm. barometric pressure.

20. Which of the following gases are lighter and which heavier than air: O_2, CO, CO_2, NH_3, and HCl?

21. Calculate the molecular weight of a substance, 1.008 g. of which occupies a volume of 220.0 cc. when collected over water at 17° C. and 710 mm. barometric pressure.

IV. Gas Law and Valence

22. A 0.33-g. sample of a metal whose atomic weight is 27 displaces from hydrochloric acid 472 cc. of hydrogen collected over water at 22° C. and 750 mm. barometric pressure. What is the valence of the metal?

23. A 0.50-g. sample of a metal whose atomic weight is 40 displaces 280 cc. of hydrogen at S.T.P. What is the valence of this metal?

24. A 7.929-g. sample of a metal whose atomic weight is 119 combines with 3.00 l. of chlorine at S.T.P. What is the valence of the metal in the resulting chloride?

25. A 3.0-g. sample of a metal whose atomic weight is 59 displaces from hydrochloric acid 1.33 l. of hydrogen collected over water at 27° C. and 747 mm. What is the valence of this metal?

V. Gas Density and Molecular Formulas

26. A certain hydrocarbon contains 92.25 per cent carbon and 7.75 per cent hydrogen. Its density relative to hydrogen is 13. What is its formula?

27. The density of phosgene at S.T.P. is 4.416 g/l. The percentage composition is C = 12.13, O = 16.17, and Cl = 71.69 per cent. What is the formula?

28. At S.T.P. 1120 cc. of phosphorus vapor is found to weigh 6.204 g. What is the number of atoms of phosphorus present in one molecule of vapor?

29. In a certain oxide of nitrogen 4.182 g. of nitrogen is combined with 7.169 g. of oxygen. Its density relative to hydrogen is 38. What is the formula?

30. A hydride of silicon containing 9.728 per cent hydrogen has a density of 2.775 g/l. at S.T.P. What is the structural formula of this compound?

31. A certain gas, 200 cc. (S.T.P.) of which weighs 0.884 g., contains 24.2 per cent carbon, 4.04 per cent hydrogen, and 71.6 per cent chlorine. What is its formula?

VI. Reaction Equations and the Gas Laws

32. What volume of hydrogen sulfide at 27° C. and 900 mm. is required to precipitate 680 g. of As_2S_3 from a $AsCl_3$ solution?

33. What volume of carbon dioxide at 25° C. and 748 mm. is necessary to convert 5.00 g. of calcium carbonate into bicarbonate?

34. A 50.0-g. sample of pure $CaCO_3$ is treated with excess hydrochloric acid. The gas evolved is collected over water at 23° C. and 740 mm. pressure. Calculate the volume of the gas.

35. What weight of zinc is needed to prepare sufficient hydrogen to give 12.0 l. of hydrogen at 30° C. and 742 mm.?

36. A 4.000-g. sample of impure $CaCO_3$, upon treatment with excess hydrochloric acid, gives 376 cc. of CO_2 at $32°$ C. and 725 mm. What is the percentage of purity of the sample?

37. What volume of acetylene collected over water at $20°$ C. and 745 mm. is obtained by the action of water on 25 g. of calcium carbide?

VII. Reaction Equations and Solution Concentration

38. If 50.0 g. of P_2O_5 is added to enough water to yield 500 cc. of solution, what is the normality of this solution?

39. A 20.0-cc. portion of dilute sulfuric acid is treated with an excess of $BaCl_2$. The $BaSO_4$ formed weighs 0.5524 g. Calculate the normality of the acid.

40. A 1.000-g. sample of pure $CaCO_3$ requires 40.25 cc. of hydrochloric acid for complete neutralization. What is the normality of the acid?

41. What volume of 1.00 M NaCl solution is required to precipitate all the silver from a solution containing 3.25 g. of $AgNO_3$?

42. What weight of aluminum can be dissolved in 500 cc. of 6.35 N hydrochloric acid?

43. What volume of 2.5 M hydrochloric acid is required to produce 5.6 l. of chlorine (S.T.P.) by the action of manganese dioxide?

44. Suppose you were determining the purity of calcium carbonate samples by titrating with 0.1000 N hydrochloric acid. A sample of what weight should be used for the buret reading to be equal to the percentage of $CaCO_3$?

45. (a) What weight of calcium hydroxide is needed to prepare 1700 cc. of 0.25 N solution?

(b) What volume of 2.0 N sulfuric acid is needed to neutralize 200 cc. of the solution above?

(c) What is the weight of the calcium sulfate formed in (b)?

46. What weight of zinc can be dissolved by 750 cc. of 2.8 N sulfuric acid?

VIII. Reaction Equations, Density, and Percentage

47. A sample of pure sodium bicarbonate is partially decomposed to sodium carbonate by heating. If a 1.0000-g. sample of the resulting mixture requires 31.12 cc. of 0.5000 N sulfuric acid for complete neutralization, what is the percentage of the mixture?

48. One hundred grams of $CaCO_3$ is precipitated by passing air through lime water. Remembering that air normally contains 0.035 volume per cent CO_2, calculate the volume of air required.

49. What volume of ammonium hydroxide solution ($d = 0.924$ g/cc. containing 20.5 per cent NH_3 by weight) can be prepared from 200 g. of ammonium sulfate?

50. At 300° C. and 1 atmosphere, 97 per cent of a sample of PCl_5 dissociates according to the equation

$$PCl_5 = PCl_3 + Cl_2$$

Calculate the percentage by weight of free chlorine in this equilibrium mixture. (*Hint:* Start with one mole of PCl_5.)

51. Hydrochloric acid whose specific gravity is 1.10 contains 20.0 per cent HCl. What volume of this solution can be made from the HCl produced by the action of concentrated H_2SO_4 on 18.6 g. of NaCl?

IX. Molecular Formulas and Raoult's Law

52. A certain non-electrolyte has the formula $C_2H_6O_2$. What is the freezing point of a solution containing 56.0 g. of this compound in 200 g. of water?

53. A certain compound is 40.0 per cent carbon, 6.7 per cent hydrogen, and 53.3 per cent oxygen. A solution of 3.00 g. of this compound in 50 g. of water freezes at $-0.62°$ C. Calculate the formula of this compound.

54. A certain compound is 8.76 per cent hydrogen, 52.1 per cent oxygen, and 39.1 per cent carbon. Of this compound 3.07 g. lowers the freezing point of 500 g. of water 0.124° C. What is the formula of the compound?

55. A certain organic compound is 52.2 per cent carbon, 13.0 per cent hydrogen, and 34.8 per cent oxygen. A solution of 0.594 g. of this compound in 100 cc. of water freezes at $-0.24°$ C. What is the formula of the compound?

X. Density, Percentage, and Concentration of Solutions

56. What volume of nitric acid having a density of 1.4 g/cc. and containing 68 per cent HNO_3 is required to prepare 1500 cc. of 2.6 N solution?

57. All the sulfur in 100 kg. of an ore containing 5.0 per cent Cu_2S is converted into sulfuric acid.

(*a*) Write equations for the reactions involved.
(*b*) Calculate the weight of hydrogen sulfate formed.
(*c*) What volume of 50 per cent sulfuric acid solution ($d = 1.4$ g/cc.) can be prepared.

58. Hydrochloric acid whose specific gravity is 1.126 contains 24.9 per cent HCl. If 100 cc. of this acid is diluted to 350 cc., what is the normality of the diluted solution?

59. A 20.00 per cent solution of ammonium sulfate has a specific gravity of 1.115. What is the molarity of this solution?

60. A 2.50 M solution of $MgCl_2$ has a specific gravity of 1.18. What is the percentage of $MgCl_2$ in this solution?

61. Nitric acid containing 68 per cent HNO_3 has a density of 1.4 g/cc. Calculate the molar concentration and the normality of this acid.

XI. General Problems

62. Air is 21 per cent oxygen by volume. What is the percentage of oxygen in air by weight?

63. If 250 cc. (S.T.P.) of a mixture of oxygen and helium weighs 0.225 g., what is the percentage of oxygen in the mixture?

64. A mixture of gases contains 15 per cent nitrogen, 36 per cent nitric oxide, and 49 per cent nitrogen dioxide. What is the weight of 1.0 l. (S.T.P.) of this gaseous mixture?

65. All the sulfur in 1000 kg. of an ore containing 5.0 per cent FeS_2 is converted into sulfuric acid.

  (a) Write equations for the reactions involved.
  (b) Calculate the weight of the hydrogen sulfate formed.
  (c) What volume of 60 per cent sulfuric acid ($d = 1.5$ g/cc.) can be prepared?

66. To what volume must 1 l. of 0.120 N sodium hydroxide solution be diluted in order that each cubic centimeter of the diluted solution be equivalent to 0.000729 g. of hydrochloric acid?

67. Ammonium hydroxide solution containing 35 per cent NH_4OH has a specific gravity of 0.89. Calculate the normality of the solution. What weight of ammonium chloride is required to yield sufficient ammonia to make 600 cc. of this solution?

68. What will be the normality of an acid solution made by mixing the following volumes of nitric acid?

> 160 cc. of 0.305 N solution
> 300 cc. of 0.503 N solution
> 220 cc. of 0.427 N solution

69. What weight of aluminum can be dissolved by 500 cc. of 6.35 N hydrochloric acid?

70. What volume of 3.5 N ammonium hydroxide solution is required to precipitate all the iron, as $Fe(OH)_3$, from a solution containing 1.0 g. of $Fe_2(SO_4)_3 \cdot 9H_2O$?

71. The oxide of a certain element E is found to contain 50 per cent oxygen. A 500-cc. sample of the gaseous oxide weighs 1.478 g. (S.T.P.). (*a*) What is the equivalent weight of the element? (*b*) What is the molecular weight of the oxide? (*c*) What is the formula for the oxide?

72. What volume of carbon dioxide at 25° C. and 748 mm. is necessary to convert 5.00 g. of calcium carbonate into the bicarbonate?

73. The density of diamond is 3.5 g/cc. A carat is 0.20 g. What is the volume of the Regent diamond whose weight is 136 carats?

74. What volume of 2.0 N acetic acid is required to react with 30 cc. of ethyl alcohol whose density is 0.77 g/cc.?

75. A mixture of nitrogen, oxygen, and argon contains 25 per cent nitrogen, 25 per cent oxygen, and 50 per cent argon by volume. What is the percentage composition of the mixture by weight?

76. A sample of hydrated sodium carbonate weighing 8.58 g. loses, when heated, 5.40 g. of water. What is the formula of the hydrate?

77. A sample of impure limestone weighing 2.4912 g. furnishes 0.0456 g. of Fe_2O_3. What is the percentage of iron in the sample?

78. What weight of NaOH is equivalent to the NaCl required to precipitate AgCl from 1.000 g. of $AgNO_3$?

79. What is the percentage composition of a brass containing only Cu, Pb, and Zn, if a 1.0000-g. sample furnishes 0.0046 g. of $PbSO_4$, and 0.8216 g. of $ZnNH_4PO_4$?

80. What weight of water is contained in a pound of Epsom salt?

81. A 5.00-g. sample of pure dolomite ($CaCO_3 \cdot MgCO_3$) is treated with hydrochloric acid until there is no further action. Calculate (*a*) the volume of gas evolved and (*b*) the percentage of Mg in the sample.

82. What is the empirical formula of a mineral containing 21.53 per cent potassium oxide, 23.55 per cent aluminum oxide, and 55.12 per cent silicon dioxide?

83. A 1.2-g. sample of impure bauxite produces 0.30 g. of aluminum. Calculate the percentage of purity of the bauxite ($Al_2O_3 \cdot 2H_2O$).

84. During the first week of 1939, 100 tons of gold was shipped from England to the United States. Its value was $36.00 per ounce and its density is 19.3 g/cc. Calculate the value and the volume of this gold.

85. What is the maximum weight of potassium permanganate that can be produced from 100 tons of an ore containing 2.5 per cent manganese?

86. What volume of (*a*) oxygen and (*b*) air are necessary for the complete combustion of 5.00 l. of acetylene?

87. A sample of pure carbon weighing 10.00 g. is burned in 30.0 l (S.T.P.) of oxygen. Calculate the percentage-by-volume composition of the mixture after combustion.

88. A thin glass bulb containing 10.0 g. of ethyl ether is broken in a 10-l. stoppered flask containing air at 1 atmosphere pressure. The temperature is 27° C. Calculate the increase in pressure due to the vaporization of the ether.

89. A 512-g. sample of CaC_2 is placed in a 10-l. steel drum and enough water added to keep the total volume of liquid and solid to 1.00 l. after all the CaC_2 has reacted. Calculate (a) the weight of C_2H_2 generated and (b) the pressure exerted on the container at 27° C.

90. Does 100 g. of $KClO_3$ or 100 g. of KNO_3 contain a greater amount of oxygen? Which of these will yield more oxygen when heated to decomposition?

91. If 22.5 g. of an element whose atomic weight is 75 combines with 0.90 g. of hydrogen, what is its valence?

92. A 0.595-g. sample of a liquid when evaporated forms 112 cc. of vapor measured at 1520 mm. and 273° C. What is the molecular weight of the vapor? Is this necessarily the molecular weight of the substance in the liquid state?

93. To heat 10 g. of a certain metal from 10° C. to 20° C. requires 4.5 cal. A 2.315-g. sample of this metal forms 2.715 g. of oxide. Calculate the atomic weight of the metal.

94. What weight of iodine is contained in 12 tons of crude Chilean saltpeter which contains 0.30 per cent $NaIO_3$?

95. What weight of crude FeTe containing 60 per cent FeTe is necessary to prepare 120 cc. H_2Te measured at 220° C. and 740 mm.?

96. (a) What volume (S.T.P.) of hydrogen chloride gas is required to neutralize a solution made by mixing 300 cc. of 2.00 N NaOH, 200 cc. 1.55 N NaOH, and 500 cc. of 3.10 N NaOH? (b) What is the weight of the NaCl formed?

97. (a) What weight of carbon must be added to 80 tons of iron to give a steel containing 1.0 per cent carbon? (b) A certain ferro-chrome alloy contains 30.0 per cent chromium. What weight of this alloy must be added to 100 tons of iron to yield a 5.0 per cent chrome steel?

98. A certain gaseous compound of carbon and hydrogen contains 75 per cent carbon. The density of the gas is 0.714 g/l. at S.T.P. What is the true molecular formula?

99. What volume of hydrogen sulfide measured at 25° C. and 750 mm. pressure is required to precipitate 10.0 g. of cupric sulfide from a cupric chloride solution?

100. In an experiment it is found that 1000 cc. of hydrogen reacts with 1000 cc. of chlorine to yield 2000 cc. of hydrogen chloride. All volumes are measured under laboratory conditions 22° C. and 750 mm.

(a) What weight of hydrogen chloride is obtained?

(b) Determine the molecular weight of hydrogen chloride.

(c) Determine the percentage composition of hydrogen chloride.

(d) Determine the true formula of hydrogen chloride.

(e) What does this experiment prove about the number of atoms of chlorine in the chlorine molecule?

The hydrogen chloride is dissolved in enough water to make 100 cc. of solution.

(f) What is the molar concentration of this solution?

(g) What volume of 0.500 N sodium hydroxide solution is required to neutralize this acid solution?

(h) What is the molar concentration of the salt solution formed?

(i) Assuming the salt to be 95 per cent ionized in this solution, calculate the freezing point of the solution.

(j) How much MnO_2 and H_2SO_4 are required to set free all the chlorine from this salt?

(k) What volume of chlorine under laboratory conditions is obtained? Compare this with the original volume.

(l) If the sulfuric acid used in part (j) has a density of 1.84 g/cc. and is 93.2 per cent H_2SO_4, what volume is necessary?

XII. Ionization and Solubility Product

101. The solubility of cadmium sulfide is 8.6×10^{-13} g/l. What is its solubility product constant?

102. The solubility product constant of lead chromate is 1.8×10^{-14}. What is the solubility of this salt in (a) moles per liter, and (b) grams per liter?

103. The ionization constant of acetic acid is 1.8×10^{-5}. What is the concentration of the hydrogen ion in a 0.50 N solution of this acid?

104. The solubility product constant of AgI is 1.7×10^{-16}. How many silver ions are there in a liter of a saturated solution of this salt?

105. The solubility of CuS is 8.8×10^{-21} g/l. What is the solubility product constant of CuS?

106. A solution containing 5.0 g. of $AgNO_3$ is made 1.0 M in HCl giving a total volume of 200 cc. What weight of Ag^+ remains in solution? $[Ag^+][Cl^-] = 1.2 \times 10^{-10}$.

107. The solubility of $Mg(OH)_2$ is 1.2×10^{-2} g/l. What is the solubility product constant of $Mg(OH)_2$?

108. If a 1.0 M solution of NH_4OH is 0.43 per cent ionized, what is the ionization constant for NH_4OH?

109. The ionization constant of acetic acid is 1.8×10^{-5} What is the per cent ionization in a 0.10 M solution?

110. What is the concentration of hydrogen ions in a 0.10 M acetic acid solution which is 1.0 M with respect to sodium acetate?

111. What weight of NH_4Cl must be added to 200 cc. of 1.0 M NH_4OH solution to prevent the precipitation of $Mg(OH)_2$ when 3.0 g. of $MgCl_2$ is added? (See problem 107.)

112. In a saturated solution of H_2S, $[H^+]^2[S^=] = 1 \times 10^{-23}$. (a) What is the concentration of the $S^=$? (b) What is the concentration of $S^=$ in a 0.3 M solution of HCl saturated with H_2S? (c) If 3 g. of $FeSO_4$ is added to 200 cc. of the solution in (b), will FeS precipitate? The solubility product constant of FeS is 1×10^{-19}.

113. The ionization constant of hypochlorous acid is 6×10^{-8} and that of acetic acid is 1.8×10^{-5}. What concentration of acetic acid has the same concentration of H^+ as a 1.0 M solution of hypochlorous acid?

114. The solubility product constants of As_2S_3 and SnS are both essentially the same (6×10^{-29}), yet their solubilities are considerably different. Explain.

115. Is the freezing point of a saturated solution of silver acetate lower than that of a saturated solution of silver chromate? The solubility product constants of these two salts are 2×10^{-3} and 2×10^{-12} respectively.

116. The solubility product constant of MnS is 1.4×10^{-15}. What is the solubility of this salt?

117. The solubility product constant of $Fe(OH)_3$ is 1.1×10^{-36}. What volume of (a) water and (b) 1.0 N hydrochloric acid is required to dissolve 1.0 g. of this hydroxide?

118. The ionization constant of HCN is 7×10^{-10} and that of HIO is 1×10^{-11}. What is the concentration of the hydrogen ion in a solution which is 0.1 M with respect to each of these acids?

INDEX

LOGARITHMS

Natural Numbers.	0	1	2	3	4	5	6	7	8	9	PROPORTIONAL PARTS.								
											1	2	3	4	5	6	7	8	9
10	0000	0043	0086	0128	0170	0212	0253	0294	0334	0374	4	8	12	17	21	25	29	33	37
11	0414	0453	0492	0531	0569	0607	0645	0682	0719	0755	4	8	11	15	19	23	26	30	34
12	0792	0828	0864	0899	0934	0969	1004	1038	1072	1106	3	7	10	14	17	21	24	28	31
13	1139	1173	1206	1239	1271	1303	1335	1367	1399	1430	3	6	10	13	16	19	23	26	29
14	1461	1492	1523	1553	1584	1614	1644	1673	1703	1732	3	6	9	12	15	18	21	24	27
15	1761	1790	1818	1847	1875	1903	1931	1959	1987	2014	3	6	8	11	14	17	20	22	25
16	2041	2068	2095	2122	2148	2175	2201	2227	2253	2279	3	5	8	11	13	16	18	21	24
17	2304	2330	2355	2380	2405	2430	2455	2480	2504	2529	2	5	7	10	12	15	17	20	22
18	2553	2577	2601	2625	2648	2672	2695	2718	2742	2765	2	5	7	9	12	14	16	19	21
19	2788	2810	2833	2856	2878	2900	2923	2945	2967	2989	2	4	7	9	11	13	16	18	20
20	3010	3032	3054	3075	3096	3118	3139	3160	3181	3201	2	4	6	8	11	13	15	17	19
21	3222	3243	3263	3284	3304	3324	3345	3365	3385	3404	2	4	6	8	10	12	14	16	18
22	3424	3444	3464	3483	3502	3522	3541	3560	3579	3598	2	4	6	8	10	12	14	15	17
23	3617	3636	3655	3674	3692	3711	3729	3747	3766	3784	2	4	6	7	9	11	13	15	17
24	3802	3820	3838	3856	3874	3892	3909	3927	3945	3962	2	4	5	7	9	11	12	14	16
25	3979	3997	4014	4031	4048	4065	4082	4099	4116	4133	2	3	5	7	9	10	12	14	15
26	4150	4166	4183	4200	4216	4232	4249	4265	4281	4298	2	3	5	7	8	10	11	13	15
27	4314	4330	4346	4362	4378	4393	4409	4425	4440	4456	2	3	5	6	8	9	11	13	14
28	4472	4487	4502	4518	4533	4548	4564	4579	4594	4609	2	3	5	6	8	9	11	12	14
29	4624	4639	4654	4669	4683	4698	4713	4728	4742	4757	1	3	4	6	7	9	10	12	13
30	4771	4786	4800	4814	4829	4843	4857	4871	4886	4900	1	3	4	6	7	9	10	11	13
31	4914	4928	4942	4955	4969	4983	4997	5011	5024	5038	1	3	4	6	7	8	10	11	12
32	5051	5065	5079	5092	5105	5119	5132	5145	5159	5172	1	3	4	5	7	8	9	11	12
33	5185	5198	5211	5224	5237	5250	5263	5276	5289	5302	1	3	4	5	6	8	9	10	12
34	5315	5328	5340	5353	5366	5378	5391	5403	5416	5428	1	3	4	5	6	8	9	10	11
35	5441	5453	5465	5478	5490	5502	5514	5527	5539	5551	1	2	4	5	6	7	9	10	11
36	5563	5575	5587	5599	5611	5623	5635	5647	5658	5670	1	2	4	5	6	7	8	10	11
37	5682	5694	5705	5717	5729	5740	5752	5763	5775	5786	1	2	3	5	6	7	8	9	10
38	5798	5809	5821	5832	5843	5855	5866	5877	5888	5899	1	2	3	5	6	7	8	9	10
39	5911	5922	5933	5944	5955	5966	5977	5988	5999	6010	1	2	3	4	5	7	8	9	10
40	6021	6031	6042	6053	6064	6075	6085	6096	6107	6117	1	2	3	4	5	6	8	9	10
41	6128	6138	6149	6160	6170	6180	6191	6201	6212	6222	1	2	3	4	5	6	7	8	9
42	6232	6243	6253	6263	6274	6284	6294	6304	6314	6325	1	2	3	4	5	6	7	8	9
43	6335	6345	6355	6365	6375	6385	6395	6405	6415	6425	1	2	3	4	5	6	7	8	9
44	6435	6444	6454	6464	6474	6484	6493	6503	6513	6522	1	2	3	4	5	6	7	8	9
45	6532	6542	6551	6561	6571	6580	6590	6599	6609	6618	1	2	3	4	5	6	7	8	9
46	6628	6637	6646	6656	6665	6675	6684	6693	6702	6712	1	2	3	4	5	6	7	7	8
47	6721	6730	6739	6749	6758	6767	6776	6785	6794	6803	1	2	3	4	5	5	6	7	8
48	6812	6821	6830	6839	6848	6857	6866	6875	6884	6893	1	2	3	4	4	5	6	7	8
49	6902	6911	6920	6928	6937	6946	6955	6964	6972	6981	1	2	3	4	4	5	6	7	8
50	6990	6998	7007	7016	7024	7033	7042	7050	7059	7067	1	2	3	3	4	5	6	7	8
51	7076	7084	7093	7101	7110	7118	7126	7135	7143	7152	1	2	3	3	4	5	6	7	8
52	7160	7168	7177	7185	7193	7202	7210	7218	7226	7235	1	2	2	3	4	5	6	7	7
53	7243	7251	7259	7267	7275	7284	7292	7300	7308	7316	1	2	2	3	4	5	6	6	7
54	7324	7332	7340	7348	7356	7364	7372	7380	7388	7396	1	2	2	3	4	5	6	6	7